Evelyn E. Harris

March 12th 1939.

THE
PHILOSOPHY OF A
BIOLOGIST

THE
PHILOSOPHY OF A
BIOLOGIST

By

J. S. HALDANE
C.H., M.D., F.R.S.

FELLOW OF NEW COLLEGE, OXFORD, AND
HONORARY PROFESSOR, UNIVERSITY OF
BIRMINGHAM; HON. LL.D., BIRMINGHAM
AND EDINBURGH; HON. D.SC., CAMBRIDGE,
DUBLIN, LEEDS, OXFORD, AND WITWATERS-
RAND

SECOND EDITION

OXFORD
AT THE CLARENDON PRESS
1936

OXFORD
UNIVERSITY PRESS
AMEN HOUSE, E.C. 4
London Edinburgh Glasgow
New York Toronto Melbourne
Capetown Bombay Calcutta
Madras Shanghai
HUMPHREY MILFORD
PUBLISHER TO THE
UNIVERSITY

FIRST PUBLISHED FEBRUARY 1935
REPRINTED MARCH 1935
SECOND EDITION 1936

PRINTED IN GREAT BRITAIN

PREFACE TO FIRST EDITION

THE present book represents an attempt to sum up shortly the conclusions which we can draw from modern philosophy. My special obligations to British contributors to post-Kantian and post-Hegelian thought will be evident, and particularly perhaps to T. H. Green and F. H. Bradley, though their names, or those of others who in this country have worked along similar lines, are scarcely mentioned in the book itself, since it is still somewhat difficult to differentiate their thought from that of their predecessors.

It is usual to classify British post-Hegelian philosophy as 'idealism', in contrast with what is regarded as the 'realism' of those for whom physical interpretation stands for a final interpretation of external reality. In this sense, but in this sense only, the book may be regarded as idealistic. In a deeper sense it is, as will be seen, wholly realistic, since it treats the universe as depicted by the sciences, not as 'mere appearance', but as the real universe imperfectly depicted.

What may be regarded as distinctive in the book is the discussion of questions relating to the fundamental conceptions applicable in the sciences, and more particularly in biology and psychology. It seems to me that such discussions are essential if we are to do justice to either the separate sciences or philosophy itself. What I have attempted is to meet this need so far as I can, and also to show in the last

chapter that religion is no mere revelation from
without, but enters into the whole of our experience
as the direct revelation in it of God.

J. S. H.

OXFORD,
January, 1935.

PREFACE TO SECOND EDITION

ON reconsidering the first edition of this book
I soon became aware of various points at which
the argument required both clarification and expan-
sion, and in this respect I am also indebted to various
reviewers and to the suggestions of philosophical
friends. In this new edition, which also seemed called
for by the unexpectedly large sale of the original
edition, I have endeavoured to embody what seemed
to be required. The main additions will be found in
Chapters II and III, and I hope they will bring out
still more clearly the philosophical importance of clear
ideas as to the fundamental conceptions and scope
of both biological and psychological science.

CONTENTS

INTRODUCTION

WHEN we survey our experience, the manner in which we view it as a whole, and the corresponding manner in which we order our lives, may be described as our philosophy. It follows that every one must have a philosophy of some sort in so far as he attempts to act consistently or rationally; and what philosophy at any stage of its development seeks for is a viewpoint from which all aspects of our existing experience may as far as possible appear consistent with one another. It therefore discusses how far any particular belief is consistent with all aspects of our experience, or requires modification to make it so. It may be consistent with part of our experience, but this is not enough.

The general objection is often made against philosophy that system follows system of philosophy, each system being destructive of its predecessor, so that philosophy represents only a vain endeavour which may be neglected safely. But this is a completely superficial view. The ideas of every important philosophical writer are based on the work of his predecessors; and that work is not lost, but carried forward in his own ideas. It is exactly the same with science as with philosophy. When new light is thrown on the general ideas previously held in any branch of science the old ideas are not destroyed, but only developed into a form which is more consistent with experience.

It is perhaps easier to realize this in the case of a science than of philosophy, since each of the sciences is less wide in its scope, and consequently better organized; but there is no real difference between science and philosophy in this respect. We can doubtless observe what are no more than changing popular fashions in philosophical opinions, as in science or art, but such mere fashions do not concern us. Nor are we much concerned with books of a philosophical character which ignore previous philosophical development, and are thus in reality out of date.

Philosophical ideas are essentially bound up with ideas applied in all branches of knowledge. Progress in philosophy implies progress in these branches, and vice versa. This follows from the fact that the experience of which philosophy endeavours to give a coherent account is presented in special forms which different branches of science confer upon it. These different forms furnish philosophy with its material, and the need for philosophy arises from the fact that the presentations as they initially stand are found not to be consistent with one another. Apart from the sciences there would be no philosophy. The task of philosophy is to bring the separate presentations into consistency with one another, and this necessarily influences them all, in at any rate some degree. Physical science, for instance, presents us with one form of knowledge, whereas the study of human behaviour in ordinary life and in history presents us with another very different and apparently contradictory form.

What we call 'common sense' flits easily from one to another of these inconsistent forms of knowledge, with only a dim realization of their inconsistencies.

At any stage of human culture the function of philosophy is to bring consistency into the different accounts, so that we can make a more rational use of each of them. If we just mix them up together the result is not only unintelligible, but produces sooner or later very serious confusion in practical affairs.

It is not the intention of this book to discuss philosophy as it has appeared among different nations and at different times, but only as it seems to the writer to appear at present in European and American civilization. The book, moreover, only discusses its subject-matter in broad outlines, and in as few words as possible.

We can best form an idea of the present-day aspect of philosophy by surveying briefly the course of philosophical development in Europe since the seventeenth century, in conjunction with the development of science. Before this time philosophy and theology were so closely associated that philosophy could hardly be distinguished from prevailing theological ideas. With the realization in Renaissance times of how much pre-Christian civilization had meant, but more particularly with the rapid development of physical science and physical conceptions in the time of Galileo and his scientific successors, contradicting, as these conceptions did, many accepted theological ideas, the need arose for more adequate philosophy.

The attempt to meet this need took its first systematic form in the writings of Descartes (1596–1650), a philosopher who also made very important contributions to mathematical and physical science. It was mainly the development of physical science that gave rise to modern European philosophy, so that the discussion may fittingly begin with this aspect of the subject.

Christian theology, which had furnished Europe with what may be regarded as a wonderfully successful common-sense view of experience, had definitely broken down in many matters of detail, and this became further accentuated in more recent times.

I

PHILOSOPHY AND PHYSICAL SCIENCE

THE chief problem which philosophy presented to Descartes was the manner in which the universe as apparently revealed by the new physical science is related to the mind or soul as apparently revealed in the facts of conscious behaviour. Descartes gave what seemed to him to be good reasons for not doubting either the independent reality of the physical universe or the equally independent reality of the spiritual world of minds or souls, subject to their original creation by God; and he proceeded to discuss the manner in which they are related, as well as their own nature. He endeavoured to present a clear general conception of the physical world, including the living body, up to a point within the brain (which he thought must be the pineal gland, since it is an unpaired structure) at which it makes contact with the soul. On the other hand, he similarly endeavoured to conceive the spiritual world up to the point at which the soul communicates with the body, and so with the surrounding physical world.

For those who have not realized the philosophical development since Descartes the general conception which he presented of the relationship of mind to body, or subject to objects, or conscious experience to physical events, remains substantially as it appeared to him. We can see this from much of recent popular and theological literature, as well as from the fact that physicists and chemists have on the whole, at least until very recent times, accepted the separation of a spiritual from a physical world. But how, if this is so, these two worlds enter into communication with one another seems a very difficult question, which is left entirely obscure.

The theoretical account which Descartes gave of the living body and its development, particularly his account of the brain, represented the body as an elaborate piece of mechanism. We can very soon see that such an account left not much place for the influence of an independent mind or soul on conscious behaviour. Descartes, indeed, concluded that animals are mere physical machines without consciousness, in spite of the fact that at least the higher animals appear to us as if they are fully conscious.

It was thus natural that one direction in which subsequent philosophy developed was towards what, roughly speaking, may be called materialism—the conclusion that not only animal, but also human behaviour can be regarded as mere physical behaviour in so far as it issues in what appears to us as voluntary action. As, however, we are aware of our perceptions and voluntary acts, we must also assume that physical phenomena in at least some parts of the brain are accompanied by consciousness. But this may be regarded as a mere 'epiphenomenon', which does not affect in any way the physical processes.

Since Descartes wrote, our ordinary ideas of what

we regard as the physical world have been greatly developed and clarified, particularly by Newton, by the development of chemical conceptions on the lines laid down by Lavoisier and Dalton, and by the emergence about the middle of last century of a clear conception of energy. But, until quite recently, these developments have been along the general lines embodied in the writings of Descartes, and thus fitted in with materialism. It is hardly necessary to refer to these developments here, as they are well described in books dealing with the history of physical science. Nor will the development of mathematics be referred to, since this development had but little to do directly with modern philosophy.

Various writers of the eighteenth century, and onwards to the present time, particularly among theoretical psychologists, have adopted the materialistic conclusion; and it has received apparent confirmation since the latter half of the nineteenth century through the general acceptance as fact that all forms of life have evolved from conditions in which no life can be distinguished. On the other hand, it was generally believed up to about the same time that various known lower forms of life originate quite commonly from inorganic conditions; but, since Pasteur's time, this belief has ceased to be held by any one. In the next chapter the conception that life can, as Descartes thought, be regarded as a physical process will be discussed fully.

Soon after Descartes, Spinoza (1632–77) drew the

conclusion that apparent conscious existence and apparent physical existence are only aspects or 'modes' of ultimate reality or 'substance', and that the two aspects are everywhere present, constituting in their union the existence of God. This, however, left the relationship of the two aspects entirely obscure, and in the effort at definition became a materialistic form of pantheism. There was nevertheless an element of profound truth in Spinoza's contention, as will appear later.

Reflection on the apparent relation of physical phenomena to conscious experience took on another direction, particularly in Great Britain. Locke (1632–1704) and Berkeley (1685–1753), like Descartes, did not doubt the independent existence of minds or souls. Locke argued that our ideas of things are formed from our actual experience of the physical world, the primitive state of the mind being that of a *tabula rasa*. He also thought that in what we perceive we can distinguish 'primary' qualities, which represent what is actually in the surrounding world, from 'secondary' qualities such as colour and smell, which are only inherent in ourselves, though produced by external physical causes.

Berkeley, however, pointed out rightly that, assuming all our knowledge to be derived from our sensations or conscious experiences, we have no right to infer the existence of a physical universe which is outside and independent of them. The real world is thus a world of sentient beings and their conscious experiences. We cannot infer the existence of a physical universe outside them. Included among the sentient beings is God, who is also regarded as the source, and at the same time a subject, of the experiences which we interpret as those of a physical world. God is consequently also the source of the orderliness we find in them. They exist in God, and not merely in finite souls, so that their existence is independent of finite experience.

This direction of development was carried further by Hume (1711–76), who argued very logically that though men commonly assume the existence of both a self-existent physical world and an equally self-existent spiritual world, all that we really experience consists of sensations, impressions, or, to use a later term, sense-data; and what we call our minds or souls are only successions of them. Hence we cannot argue legitimately to the existence of anything beyond these sense-data, though we find that for some unknown reason sense-data are associated together in coherent successions, which we call minds, and different sense-data are associated in certain characteristic ways which physical science describes. Thus neither materialism nor spiritual idealism seems possible.

Our universe is the universe of our direct experience supplemented by imagination including memory; but in it we gradually discover an orderliness which is independent of what we wish for, or at first expect, and which it seems only common sense to attribute to the existence of a physical world outside us, with certain characters of its own. It seems equally common sense to regard ourselves as independent of this physical world, but observing and influencing it. If, however, we proceed to consider how such a physical world could be perceived by us through our bodies, it then appears that all we could perceive would be the individual impressions conveyed to some part of our brains; and this leads to the sceptical conclusions of Hume, which leave us with no satisfactory means of understanding how either a physical world could appear to us as it does, or we ourselves appear to influence it. How it is that both an outside physical world, and we ourselves as observing and influencing it, appear so real is left entirely obscure.

The strait to which philosophy was reduced by the dualism which assumed definite shape in the writings of Descartes is shown by the attempt of Leibniz (1646–1716), to whose ideas further reference will be made in Chapter II, to preserve the dualism with the help of such an utterly strained conception as that of divinely pre-established harmony between what we interpret as physical phenomena and what we regard as the spiritual phenomena of conscious behaviour. The two interpretations bear no relation to one another. The truth is that the apparent common sense represented in the writings of Descartes was inconsistent with itself, so that some other conception had to be adopted.

The next great step in the history of modern philosophy is represented by the writings of Immanuel

Kant (1724–1804), a philosopher who lived quietly all his life at Königsberg, and lectured during his early life on physical science. Looked at as a whole, Kant's reasoning points to a way of escape from the inconsistencies involved in the attempts of his predecessors to reconcile the apparent physical world with the apparent spiritual world of perception and volition. For this reason his ideas have formed a basis for all really new philosophical developments since his time.

In his *Critique of Pure Reason* Kant discusses experience as interpreted physically. He points out something which his predecessors had not realized, but which becomes quite evident as soon as our attention is drawn to it. This is that all the data of our perception of physical phenomena embody relationships to other phenomena. An isolated sensation or sense-datum, such as Locke, Berkeley, Hume, and others had imagined, is therefore a mere empty product of imagination. Thus perceptions exist only relatively to one another as regards their arrangement in time or space; are qualitatively and quantitatively related to one another; are related as expressing substances and properties, causes and effects, or reciprocal actions. We cannot build up these relationships out of simpler elements, since the simpler elements do not exist. The relationships are inherent in what is perceived, and it is these inherent relationships which give form and consistency to what is perceived. In the fact of perception they are read into what is perceived. The different kinds of relationships, or of principles embodied in physical interpretation, are designated as 'categories' by Kant, and he gives a list of what he considered them to be, though he specially distinguishes relations of time and space as forms of perception.

Hence the world of perception appears to us as a physically interpretable universe, though it is perception itself that gives its form and coherency to this universe. It is therefore, Kant thought, only a phenomenal world, and the conception of self-existent individual things or events in it has no ultimate meaning. But this account throws no light on why the physically consistent details of this phenomenal universe are just what they are. With equal physical consistency they might be quite different. Kant therefore concluded that beyond the phenomenal physical universe there must be a 'noumenal' world of real existence, which, however, it is impossible to perceive.

The fact of the relationships embodied in all that is perceived involves the existence of unity within which the relationships exist; and since it is the world as perceived which this unity embraces, we must call it mind.

It will thus be seen that for Kant the perceived physical universe was no longer, as it was for Descartes, and appears still to be for uncritical thought, a universe independent of perception of it, and therefore outside of mind, but a universe to which the relationships which are present in perception, and therefore belong to mind, give its form, and thus enter into its constitution. This mind can, however, be no mere mind or soul existing here and now in space and time, but mind in the sense of unity within which exist the perceived relationships of space and time, and all the other relationships which give form to the physically interpreted universe of our conscious experience. Outside the phenomenal universe there is, for Kant, nothing that can be perceived, simply because perception implies the relationships.

The phenomenal world of experience is, therefore, not a world independent of mind as Descartes assumed, but a world into the constitution of which mind in the sense indicated enters at every point. To this extent Kant's conclusions can be regarded as idealistic, though he held to the idea of a 'noumenal' world which is entirely outside the possibility of our perceiving it.

In his *Critiques of Practical Reason*, and of *Judgement*, Kant goes much further than in his *Critique of Pure Reason*; and his general philosophical position cannot be judged, as is sometimes attempted, apart from these further *Critiques*. When we consider the *Critique of Pure Reason* by itself, however, we can regard it as a rehabilitation of the physical interpretation of our experience, in face of the difficulties which previous philosophical writers, and particularly Hume, had pointed out in it. It was rehabilitated, however, as a phenomenal universe, the only universe of which we can actually have experience. We interpret and perceive it as a physical universe because mind is so constituted that we cannot interpret and perceive it otherwise. Mind is without position or bounds in space and time, since space and time themselves are manifestations of mind, and are thus within it. For philosophy there were now no immensities of space and time outside of mind.

Kant's philosophical successors in Germany, Great Britain, Italy, and elsewhere have further developed his reasoning, and we must now refer generally to these developments. Fichte, Schelling, and Hegel (1770–1831) pointed out that Kant's distinction between a phenomenal and noumenal universe cannot be upheld. His noumenal world is only a remnant of the supposed self-existent physical universe which philosophical reasoning had shown to be meaningless. Thus the unifying element of which Kant had pointed out the existence as mind in his phenomenal world must be inherent in all that is real, so that it is the expression of one Absolute Being. The conception of 'the Absolute' thus came to play an essential part in post-Kantian philosophy, and its relation to, or identity with, the religious conception of God was often discussed.

A further criticism of Kant was that his 'categories' were incomplete, and by no means covered the universe of our perception. We perceive for instance living organisms, persons, and all that pertains to them. There was no room in Kant's world of perception except for what physical science recognizes, whereas what we actually perceive includes much that physical science gives no coherent account of, and does not attempt to interpret.

Another line of criticism, developed particularly by Hegel, was that the categories which enter into our experiences cannot be regarded as otherwise than interconnected. Hegel maintained that they develop logically one from another—the higher from the lower. In his *Logic* he endeavoured to trace the course of this development. As will appear below, we must accept as a fact that the conceptions which are applied in the formation of our perceived experience are essentially interdependent; but the Hegelian attempt to show that they develop logically out of one another has evoked but little lasting support. The artificiality of this attempt became evident in its application to details, as in his *Philosophy of Nature*.

Hegel's attempt to deduce logically the general nature of the concrete world of perception may be criticized from another standpoint. The elements which we distinguish in our perceived experience are no mere logical elements, but have also a motive aspect embodying will. Hence we cannot describe our experience in terms of mere logic or ideas. As was maintained by Schopenhauer, will is embodied in our perceived universe, and not mere logic. In the succeeding chapters this will become more clear. Our universe is more than, to repeat Bradley's graphic expression, an 'unearthly ballet of bloodless categories'.

The conclusions of Kant's *Critique of Pure Reason* were completely consistent with the conceptions in accordance with which physical science interpreted, and continued during the nineteenth century to interpret in a more clearly developed form, what we call the physical universe. He had simply given a philosophical interpretation to those conceptions, thus avoiding the difficulties involved in the dualism of Descartes. Some rather serious difficulties were found to exist in the application of the conceptions in question to physical phenomena, but did not come clearly to the surface till the end of the century.

From the standpoint of post-Kantian philosophy, rejecting Kant's narrow conception of the categories which enter into the constitution of perceived experience, physics could be regarded as a science dealing with only certain parts of experience, corresponding to Kant's 'phenomenal' world, and entirely neglecting other parts. This neglect seemed justified in practice owing to the apparent fact that the sphere of mere physical interpretation can be so limited that within this sphere anything further than physical interpretation is unnecessary. Thus questions involving life or personality are not dealt with in physics, so that the fundamental limitation on which physical interpretation is based can be left out of consideration in physics, though certainly not in philosophy.

One of the difficulties just referred to is in connexion with the manner in which light or any other form of electromagnetic wave appears to travel. It had hitherto been assumed that these waves exist in a relatively stationary 'ether', within which all movements are occurring; and the astronomical observations hitherto made had seemed consistent with this assumption. But if this is correct the times taken by a light-impulse to travel to a mirror and back must differ according to the different directions in which the mirror and observer are apparently travelling, and the correspondingly varying apparent velocities. The differences can be calculated, and observed differences ought to give a measure of the differing apparent velocities with which the mirror and observer are travelling. With the delicate methods now available such differences could be measured directly. Actual measurements were made by Michelson and Morley in 1887, but they gave what then seemed the astounding result that the measured velocity of light is always the same, in whatever direction, and at whatever apparent speed, the mirror and observer are moving in relation to the direction of the light-impulse. It was as if the surrounding universe, as hitherto conceived, was simply mocking the observer; and relativity, as Kant had conceived it, and a Newtonian physicist could accept it, was of no avail in solving the difficulty.

It was Einstein who offered a satisfactory solution; and he did so by means of a far-reaching development of the principle of relativity. He pointed out that not only are the motions of bodies relative only to the positions of other bodies, but that we must regard the lapse of time as having no meaning except as an index of their motions relatively to distant bodies. On any particular body time will thus go faster or slower, according as the body is moving towards or away from distant bodies. If we are travelling in the same direction as a light-impulse which we send out, the time taken by it to go to a mirror and return will thus be lengthened as compared with that taken by an impulse sent out in the opposite direction; and the difference will exactly account for the observed fact that the two impulses take the same time to go and return, though on the old relativity conception one would take longer than the other. There is therefore, evidently, no meaning in absolute flow of time or simultaneity, just as there is, on Kantian relativity principles, no meaning in absolute motion or rest.

Thus the extended principle of relativity modifies essentially our conception of time. But it equally modifies our conception of space. As applied to the Michelson-Morley experiment, the result is the same as if distances were shortened in the same direction as the earth is moving relatively to the positions of distant bodies; and all measurements of length are similarly dependent on relative velocity of movement. We cannot, therefore, separate spatial measurements from time measurements, so that time must be regarded as an additional dimension of space, since otherwise space is insufficiently defined, as well as time.

But the new principle of relativity carries us still

farther. The earth is in even rotation relatively to bodies around it, and in view of the principle of inertia objects should tend to fly off at a tangent from the earth, and the planets from the sun. We have hitherto regarded this as being prevented by the 'force' of gravitation, acting at a distance in the manner described by Newton. The idea of such a force acting at a distance is, however, far from intelligible, and Einstein pointed out that we can dispense with this idea completely if we assume that the space surrounding matter is modified or distorted in such a manner that other matter which approaches is diverted in the same manner as if gravitation existed. The idea of either space or time being capable of what might be called local alteration or distortion would have seemed incredible to us apart from the previous demonstration with regard to time; but this is no longer the case, and it simplifies our ideas if we regard space as being modified round matter in the manner just indicated. It gets rid of gravitational action at a distance, and at the same time enables us to account for mass measured by weight being the same as mass measured by its inertia. Why these two measurements should give the same results had hitherto been unknown.

If this manner of regarding the relations of space to mass is correct, it will follow, among certain other things, that the path of light passing near the sun towards us will be diverted to a very appreciable extent. The fact of this diversion was verified in eclipse observations, and Einstein's conception of the relationship of space to matter is now accepted generally by physicists, though a working out of this conception in connexion with electromagnetic phenomena has not yet been reached.

To those philosophical students who were familiar with Kant's applications of the principle of relativity Einstein's extension of this principle appealed at once. Kant conceived the relationships which give form to the perceived universe as so many separable relationships constituting together his 'forms of perception' and 'categories'. Einstein's discoveries showed, in at least part, that these forms and categories are not separable from one another, but imply one another.

It follows from Einstein's conception of the relation of space to mass that if the matter in the universe is limited, and concentrated round some point, space must be curved round this point, and is limited, though not bounded, owing to this fact. On the other hand, spectroscopic examination of the very numerous nebulae visible or capable of being photographed with very powerful telescopes proves that all of them, as shown by the well-known Doppler effect, are receding from us rapidly, or we from them, and that the farther away they are, the more rapidly are they receding. Thus if we regard the universe as limited spatially, we must also regard it as continuously expanding. The most probable physical explanation of this seems to be that of Milne, according to which part of the matter in a primitive intensely hot gaseous state would constantly be flying off free. The particles flying off fastest would get farthest before forming nebulae, which would continue afterwards to fly relatively fast.

In the world of experience there can be no greater velocity than that of light, since an impulse travelling away from us or towards us at a greater velocity than that of light would not be perceived as travelling. The universe which is capable of being perceived is the only universe which has any meaning for us.

Einstein's application of the theory of relativity is more far-reaching in detail than that of Kant, the result being that certain relationships embodied in the perceived universe are essentially interconnected, so that they only exist in the interconnexion. Spatial relations are thus not separable from time-relations, nor from those of mass or mutual movement, whereas on Kant's conception these relationships were separable and independent of one another. For Einstein, as for Kant, the physical universe is essentially a unified universe, nothing being self-existent. In this sense modern physics may be said to have become idealistic, although, as with post-Kantian philosophy, not in the sense that the universe as perceived depends on any mere individual percipient. But if we say that it exists in the perceptions of God, we must also say that individual perception must participate in some way in Divine perception, though how this can be so, and what meaning can be attached to perception which is not mere individual perception, is left entirely obscure. This question will be taken up again in Chapter IV. What seems plain from the standpoint of relativity physics is that our universe represents an all-embracing unity; but identification of this unity with God implies for relativity physics, as for any argument based solely on Kant's *Critique of Pure Reason*, nothing with regard to the nature of God except all-embracing unity.

In a yet further respect the universe for recent physics has come to differ from that of Kant or the nineteenth century. One discovery after another has shown that what was previously taken as inert matter is in reality a centre of intense activity.

We may first consider the case of atoms and the molecules formed by their union. It was pointed out by J. J. Waterston in a paper presented to the Royal Society in 1845, but referred to the *Archives* (where it was available for consultation, though it was at the time disregarded as being inconsistent with what was then the orthodox scientific conception of heat), that a gas behaves just as would a swarm of perfectly elastic molecules travelling very fast in a chaotic manner in all directions, and that its temperature, or that of matter in any form, can be regarded as an index of the mean *vis viva* or kinetic energy of the molecules, absolute zero being the condition at which all relative molecular movement would be at a standstill. This was the kinetic theory of gases and temperature, afterwards brought forward by others and generally accepted. It is a theory wholly consistent with either the Newtonian or Kantian conception of the perceived physical universe, as capable of being regarded as containing what are essentially inert units of matter, apart from their attractions for one another.

This conception has been undermined in various ways. The discovery of radio-active substances by the Curies and others showed that, in addition to the energy which can be regarded as heat, atoms contain immense stores of internal energy which still persists in them in spite of the extremest falls of temperature. It has also been shown that as solid bodies cool they cease to lose energy in proportion to the fall in temperature. Monatomic gases do not, moreover, take up or lose kinetic energy of rotation at any ordinary temperature.

The study of electrical discharges in vacuum tubes has led J. J. Thomson, Rutherford, and others to the conception of atoms as consisting of constellations of 'electrons', negatively charged, rotating with enormous velocity round positively charged central cores. The latter, in view of chemical and other evidence, must be regarded as containing, in the case of each elementary atom, a certain number of 'protons', a proton being the relatively simple sort of central core contained in an atom of hydrogen, the lightest element. The existence of 'neutrons' and 'positrons' has been established more recently.

Closer study of the radiation of heat, light, and other forms of what had been interpreted as electromagnetic waves has led Planck and others to the conclusion that radiation is given off and absorbed in definite units or 'quanta'. This introduces into the conception of energy the further conception that, like matter, it occurs in definite units. A ray of light can thus be resolved into light-quanta. Radiation must also be conceived as possessing mass, however small. We are thus brought back, in part, to Newton's original conception that a ray of light is a stream of minute particles, travelling with enormous velocity. These particles, if they be called such, must also be regarded, in view of all the evidence for the undulatory theory of light, as waves. But it has recently been shown that electrons also have the properties of waves as well as particles; and atoms also appear to consist of waves. Electrons seem in some respects to behave as if they were definite particles, and in other respects as waves. Here the old physical conceptions seem to fail us even more definitely than was already the case. Matter and motion seem as if they are inseparable as facts, and in their inseparable form they display co-ordinated wave-activity, though the waves are not oscillations of particles, nor are the apparent particles anything apart from the oscillations. The science of physics appears to possess at present no definite word to describe the new facts of observation which are now forced upon it, and perhaps it may become necessary to go to biology in search of a word.

Mechanical conceptions are still of the utmost practical use in physics, but in fundamental matters physics can no longer be said to be a mechanical science. The modern conception of relativity cuts across the idea that the universe can be regarded as consisting of self-existent matter and separable events. In all its aspects the universe of recent physical interpretation implies unity. On the other hand, the distribution of what is happening has taken on a measure of co-ordination which was absent in the older conception. The happenings in an atom, electron, proton, or light-quantum appear as no longer chaotic, or dependent on mere chance, but inherent and co-ordinated.

From the standpoint at which the kinetic theory of gases originated all activity was fundamentally unco-ordinated or chaotic, and the energy of the universe was degenerating towards a state in which its average temperature would be so uniform that no visible transference of molecular into other forms of energy could occur, and ultimately all molecular activity would cease. But from the newer standpoint co-ordinated activity is inherent in matter. With fall in temperature this inherent activity is not lost to it. As the temperature of a solid falls the proportion of energy which can be withdrawn from it by a given further fall in temperature diminishes till it becomes negligible.

If the temperature of everything became uniform there could of course be no conversion of heat into gross mechanical motion. But even if the temperature fell to absolute zero everything would still be full of co-ordinated activity; and the evidence of co-ordinated activity, in the form of definite aggregations and combinations, would be more evident than at higher temperatures. The physically interpreted universe as it appeared to the physicists of last century seemed to be progressing continuously towards a state in which activity would be at a standstill. This conclusion was embodied in what is known as the second law of thermodynamics, or the law of increasing entropy. For the new physics the universe appears in a different light. It is no longer towards a state of rest, but towards a state in which co-ordinated activity prevails over what had seemed to be nothing but chaotic activity, that the perceived universe is progressing. A gradual cooling down appears as a gradual disappearance of primitive chaos.

Physicists, unless they become philosophical, exclude the phenomena of life and conscious behaviour from their consideration. But biological phenomena and those of conscious behaviour belong to the world which we perceive, and philosophy has to bring together in some way or other the physical interpretation of the world with those of biology and psychology. The old physics, or the Kantian conception of the phenomenal world, left what seemed a complete gap between physics and biological or psychological interpretation of our experience, except on the hypothesis, which we shall see in the following chapters to be excluded, that life and conscious behaviour could be interpreted in terms of physical conceptions. For the new physics the gap appears to be no longer one which can never be bridged.

Whatever ultimate fundamental conceptions physical and chemical study may lead us to, it is nevertheless true, and seems likely to remain so, that for ordinary practical purposes the old physical conceptions, as developed along the direct lines of Galileo and Newton, will continue to be employed. As will be pointed out later, there is ample philosophical justification for this as a merely practical course; but if we seek for anything fundamental along the narrow lines of the old physical conceptions we can only meet with disappointment.

Similar disappointment must also meet us if we endeavour to make 'simple sense-data' the basis of philosophical interpretation. There are no simple sense-data or isolated elements in our experience. What we may take to be simple sense-data unrelated to the rest of experience are only imaginary entities, the ghosts of the old conception that mind and body are related to one another in a manner similar to that in which two inert bodies are related to one another according to the old mechanistic physics. The popular psychological and other literature which treats sense-data as primary isolated events, in the old pre-Kantian manner, is simply out of date.

Although the conception of relativity and other advances have brought physics into what seems possible direct touch with experience which has not hitherto been interpreted physically, the significance of this is not yet generally recognized in physical science. Some physicists are still fond of making our flesh creep by pointing to the immensities of time and space in contrast with what they represent as the microscopical smallness of all human affairs. But for philosophy since Kant, and in a still clearer sense since Einstein's discoveries, the whole world of our physical experience is a world of perceived experience, and non-existent apart from perception, though not mere individual perception. In this sense it is not outside of us, and in imagining the remotest depths of space and time we are only realizing what belongs to our own world of perception. We are no mere isolated units existing here and now in terms of an obsolete conception of the relation of mind to a physical world, but in a very real sense, which it will be the aim of the following chapters to define further, we are at home in every part of our universe of perception.

It will be shown at the same time that physical science is only an abstract branch of knowledge, applying to artificially limited aspects of our experience, and that a realization of this fact affects at every point our conception of what appears for physical science by itself as simply a physical universe. If we are aware of the limitations of physical interpretation we can continue to use it for endless practical purposes without causing confusion by endeavouring to apply it to what it cannot be applied to owing to its abstract or limited nature. We can accept the physically interpreted world as a partial representation of reality, sufficient for certain practical purposes, but quite insufficient in other respects. The next chapter will deal with an aspect of our perceived experience to which physical conceptions cannot be applied successfully.

II

PHILOSOPHY AND BIOLOGY

IT can be said truly that the significance of biological science in philosophical surveys of our experience has hitherto received only scant recognition by philosophical writers, and very little effective recognition by scientific writers, since they have for the most part been under the influence of misleading general conceptions of the subject. It will be my aim to remedy this in the present chapter. Hence a more detailed discussion will be needed than in the previous chapter.

Kant realized very clearly that physical interpretation does not exhaust the world of our experience, though he thought that it covers what he regarded as the phenomenal world of perception. In his two further Critiques he proceeded to point out that in addition to the phenomenal world of perception there is a domain of what he called aesthetic judgement, which is treated of in his *Critique of Judgement*, and a domain of practical reasoning, treated of in his *Critique of Practical Reason*.

In the *Critique of Judgement* Kant dealt with such judgements as we make with regard to life or to beauty. He concluded that we judge of an organism as a whole which expresses itself in innumerable specific particulars of form and behaviour. Yet it appeared to him that in our definite perceptions of living organisms we only discover phenomena which we can interpret in accordance with the mechanical conceptions of the physical sciences. It is the same with judgements of beauty. They embody ideas of inherent co-ordination which cannot be deduced from the perceived or physically interpreted character of what is beautiful. Yet judgements as to life and beauty have an aesthetic significance of their own; and since for Kant the physically interpreted universe was only phenomenal, this position as regards life and beauty did not seem inconsistent.

The manner in which Kant established a gulf between a phenomenal universe of perception and a universe of aesthetic judgement and moral obligation was rightly criticized by his philosophical successors, as has already been mentioned; and a close consideration of this feature in his philosophy is essential. According to Kant's account the universe as interpreted physically has no intelligible relation with what he separates off as the spheres of aesthetic judgement and moral obligation. As we shall see, this made it impossible for him to give any satisfactory account of either life or conscious behaviour. In this chapter we shall first consider physical interpretation of life, in accordance with Kant's conception of physical interpretation, compared with what he regarded as aesthetic judgement concerning life. It is here that his reasoning requires such careful scrutiny—a scrutiny which he never applied, and the absence of which in modern philosophical reasoning has led to great confusion.

We have seen that one part of the philosophy of
Descartes was that he looked upon living organisms
as only pieces of physical mechanism; and Kant assumed that from the standpoint of the phenomenal
world of perception they must be so regarded. On
this point various philosophical writers, and apparently most theologians, agreed with him. The
theologians added that living organisms are such
elaborately constructed machines that they must be
attributed to special intervention of a divine Artificer,
whereas Kant regarded any such inference from their
construction as being quite unjustifiable. He was in
as complete sympathy as was Descartes with a scientific aim of tracing the nature of their physico-chemical mechanism and the physico-chemical processes by
which they originated, of which Descartes had sug-
gested an account in one of his shorter books. Those
who were directly studying living organisms took,
however, for the most part a definitely different view
of the matter.

The publication by Descartes of his theory of the
body as a machine evoked little support on the
scientific side, but quickly led to the more definite
formulation by biologists and medical men of the
conception known as vitalism. This conception was
evidently a modern adaptation of ideas which had
been handed down from the Hippocratic writings and
Aristotle.

To Hippocrates or the Hippocratic writings we can
trace certain great ideas which placed medicine, and

by implication biology, on a sound basis for future development. He swept away various superstitious beliefs as to the cure of disease by pointing out that it is the 'nature' of a living organism to maintain and heal itself, so that medical and surgical measures are nothing mysterious, but simply aids to 'nature'. Hence the aim of medicine is by patient observation, the results of which it is the duty of medical men to preserve and communicate to their profession, to discover how nature becomes disturbed in illness and injury: to understand also her processes of recovery, and so to be able to aid her by both preventive and curative measures. In the early seventeenth century the Hippocratic tradition was generally present among medical men, but in the degraded form that 'spirits' are present in the living body, and fulfil the functions of what Hippocrates called 'nature'. Thus a 'vegetative spirit' was supposed to preside over the processes of digestion and assimilation of food, a 'vital spirit' over such activities as those of the heart or breathing, and an 'animal spirit' over nervous and emotional phenomena.

Clearly these conceptions were vague and unsatisfactory, but they at least stood for the outstanding facts embodied in the Hippocratic conception of a living organism—facts which cannot be missed in the study of living organisms. It was natural, therefore, that the representation by Descartes of the living body as a machine met with emphatic dissent, since we cannot imagine a machine which makes, maintains,

and repairs itself. The attempts of Descartes to picture such a machine were not only crude in the
extreme, but failed fundamentally in representing the
facts.

Let us see how this was so. In the light of later, and
even contemporary knowledge it is evident that the
physiology of Descartes was grossly wrong in detail.
He thought, for instance, that ordinary muscles con-
tract because they are blown up by a discharge of
'animal spirits' down nerve-tubules, the animal spirits
being separated off from the blood by a mechanical
process, and liberated in the brain down certain
nerve-tubules by afferent nerve impulses, just as light
is reflected in a certain manner, and regardless of the
fact that the nature of responses to ordinary sensory
stimuli depends on the environing conditions. In
spite of Harvey's clear proofs to the contrary, he
regarded the diastole as the active phase of the heart's
action, since this assumption was needed for his
theory of muscular contraction. His conception of
how the foetus is formed mechanically in its development was also based on no observations whatever.
But apart from all his mistakes the question remains
whether he was not right in principle in believing
that a physico-chemical explanation of the fundamental facts as to maintenance and reproduction is
both conceivable and ultimately correct. We may
discuss this mechanistic theory of life generally here,
in the light of more recent developments of it.

The mechanistic theory of reproduction may first

be considered. This implies that in the germ from which an organism develops there is such a physical and chemical structure that in contact with an environment which possesses no constant structure the adult form is built up. When we consider how definite in almost endless detail the structure of an adult organism is known to be, and how definite also are its characteristic reactions with environment, as shown in its life-history, we can see at once that the mechanistic theory of life implies amazing complication in, at any rate, a germ.

But the germ not only gives rise to the adult organism, but also to an indefinitely large succession of further germs, so that each germ must contain the necessary mechanism for making an indefinite number of further similar mechanisms. We are thus involved in the assumption of absolutely endless and totally incredible physical and chemical complication.

It is easy to ignore the difficulties completely by saying that offspring is like parent because each is developed from similar material, which was at one time called germ-plasma, and can now be specified more particularly as the chromosomes and chromomeres of a fertilized ovum. But the fundamental difficulty which led the scientific contemporaries of Descartes to reject his mechanistic physiology remains exactly the same. Any mechanistic theory of reproduction, including the reproductive processes which are constantly occurring all over the body, leads only to incoherence.

The investigations which originated with Mendel show that the germ of a cellular organism must be regarded as an organized colony of more elementary germs or 'genes', each embodying persistently reproduced differences, and contributing, unless it is absent, to the characters which are transmitted to offspring. It seems clear also that the peculiar characters of these elementary 'genes' may be intensified, modified, or rendered latent by mutual influence, and that in spite of the great persistency with which they reproduce themselves they may, in contact with their environment, undergo changes giving rise to what are known as mutations in the developing organism and its descendants.

This new knowledge as to the details of reproduction has thrown much fresh light on the subject, and proved of great practical importance in prediction. But the reproduction of genes, which takes place at every cell-division, remains just as unintelligible on a mechanistic conception of heredity as reproduction of a complete organism; and from a mechanistic standpoint there is no simplification of the problem, which now involves not merely the reproduction of individual genes, but also of their characteristic relationships to other genes and to the environment generally. Various scientific writers still speak, particularly in connexion with the new knowledge as to genes, of the 'mechanism' of heredity, but such an expression has no conceivable meaning in relation to the facts. In the exclusive light of existing physical and chemical conceptions reproduction appears as nothing less than miraculous.

Let us consider another aspect of the physiology of Descartes—his theory of the reflected or reflex activity embodied in responses to sensory or afferent stimuli. It is only in a very superficial sense that responses to afferent stimuli can be likened to reflection of light or other processes which we can with great success interpret physically. For the physiological response to a stimulus depends quite evidently on the surrounding physiological conditions, so that what can be regarded as a certain physical stimulus evokes different responses at different times. The body as a whole, or the nervous system as a whole, is involved in each response to an afferent stimulus. The response is an integrated one, in the sense that it embodies behaviour of such a nature as to represent some part of the maintenance, in face of a varying environment, of the organism's life. The response is intelligible on the theory that it is part of the continuous adaptation through which what we easily recognize as the unity of an organism's life is maintained, but not as an isolable chain of physical events, such as Descartes imagined.

In more recent times attempts have been common to base an interpretation of responses to afferent stimuli on the Cartesian theory of reflex action. But these attempts fall under the same criticism as the crude physiology of Descartes himself. They fail to represent the integrated character of the responses, and this failure is common to all attempts to represent phenomena of life as physico-chemical processes.

Soon after Descartes the prevalent ideas as to 'spirits' gave place to a somewhat simplified theory, known as 'vitalism', which as opposed to the Cartesian mechanistic theory of life first took definite scientific shape in the writings of Stahl (1660–1734), who is also well known as the author of the phlogiston theory which dominated chemistry for about a century. But Stahl believed that the soul, acting unconsciously, plays the part of what later vitalists called the 'vital principle', or 'vital force'. His position would therefore be more correctly called 'animism'. The vitalists who succeeded him held that though physical or chemical interpretations can be applied successfully to inorganic phenomena, and even to much of what can be observed within the bodies of living organisms, the characteristic phenomena of life, and particularly the manner in which living organisms maintain, heal, and reproduce themselves, are not capable of mechanistic interpretation, but are visible and tangible manifestations of the activity of the vital principle or vital force, acting as an organizing agency, but blindly, and thus differing from the soul. For each species of organism the vital principle was supposed to have special characters, and death was regarded as a disappearance of the vital principle. The latter must also be regarded as transmitted from parents to germ of a living organism, and developing with its growth.

Life implies constant activity, and the vital principle was accordingly regarded as something essentially active, constantly controlling, and therefore interfering with, physical tendencies towards disintegration of organic structure, and constantly building up new organic structure in the processes of nutrition and reproduction, and, in general, integrating the behaviour of each part. No mere physical or chemical account of essential organic processes could therefore be valid or true to nature. There was thus an essential contradiction between vitalism and Kant's conclusion that investigation of organic activity can only reveal phenomena capable of physical interpretation. According to the vitalists the phenomena actually perceived in living organisms are perceived as manifestations of what Kant relegated to an unperceived universe of aesthetic judgement.

The vitalistic attitude of John Hunter, an eminent British scientific contemporary of Kant, was typical of the prevailing attitude among biologists. Until about the middle of the nineteenth century vitalism continued to represent the usual belief among scientific men, including physicists and chemists who had given special attention to the phenomena of life. Thus not only was this true of such men as Johannes Müller, the great physiologist and comparative anatomist, or von Baer, the great embryologist, but also of great chemists, like Liebig and Wöhler, who had investigated the chemical aspect of life. It was Wöhler who discovered how to form urea outside the living body, thus getting rid of a false idea prevalent among chemists that substances formed in the living body, with the known exceptions of carbon dioxide and water, cannot be formed outside it. But this discovery, and further discoveries of the same nature, never shook his faith in vitalism, nor was there any reason why they should, though he is commonly represented as an opponent of vitalism.

Since about the middle of the nineteenth century vitalism of an acknowledged kind has, however, almost disappeared among biologists. The reason for this was by no means only the universal acceptance by biologists of the fact of evolution and the influence of natural selection on its direction, but chiefly a realization that the conception of a vital principle guiding physical phenomena within the living body has internal inconsistencies which we can readily see to be similar in nature to those in the Cartesian idea of a mind or soul in causal relationship with an independent physical world in and around the body. As soon as we investigate in detail the supposed influence of the vital principle, we find that what we had attributed to its influence depends on what the vitalists admitted to be physical and chemical influences. Apart from these influences the supposed influence of the vital principle disappears.

The life of an organism, with all its characteristic peculiarities, can be shown by an ever-increasing body of experimental evidence to be dependent on the nature of its environment, which was interpreted physically and chemically by vitalists and non-vitalists alike. Human life ceases almost at once if the oxygen supply to the central nervous system is cut off, or if the latter is reached by some very poisonous substance in quite slight concentrations. Facts such as these, which may be multiplied indefinitely, make vitalism an altogether inconsistent hypothesis.

Vitalism, moreover, was acting as a hindrance to such investigation of life as appeared to be possible with the help of physical and chemical methods, since whatever seemed for the time to be obscure tended to be attributed to something which apparently could not be investigated further, whereas actually there is no limit to the investigation of life.

In still another respect vitalism was an altogether defective working hypothesis. The conception of a vital principle could not be connected except negatively with observations as to the relations of an organism with its environment. It thus did not help in the interpretation of these relations or in their prediction. It only amounted to a negative protest against a mechanistic physiology which, as already seen, was grossly defective. A working hypothesis which throws no light on the details dealt with in any science is useless.

One of the leaders in the revolt against vitalism among the younger physiologists about the middle of last century was Theodor Schwann, Johannes Müller's assistant, and discoverer (1839) of the fact that the body of a higher animal, like that of a higher plant, is made up of the units called cells. He was an orthodox Catholic, and afterwards became a professor at the Catholic University of Louvain—an index of the association, which is also evident, for instance, in the writings of the well-known English theologian Paley, of a mechanistic theory of life with orthodox theology. Schwann believed that living cells are produced by a physico-chemical process of precipitation, so that all physiological phenomena dependent on cell-activity and cell-structure must ultimately be physical and chemical processes.

Schwann's ideas as to cell-formation were soon, however, found to be erroneous, since closer observation showed that cells are always formed by the division of pre-existing cells; and how it is that groups of cells associate themselves together to make up the very specific structures of any higher organism remained altogether obscure from a mechanistic standpoint. Soon afterwards there came the demonstration by Pasteur and others that all known forms of even the minutest of organisms arise out of pre-existing similar organisms. The fundamental objections to vitalism remained, however, and were much strengthened when J. R. Mayer pointed out in 1845 that the oxidation processes which are associated with life must be regarded as not only, as had been shown by Lavoisier, the source of the heat produced by living organisms, but also the source of the mechanical energy which they develop in muscular work or other forms of physiological activity. Hence there is no need to attribute 'active' physiological processes to the supposed vital principle. The publication in 1859 of Darwin's *Origin of Species* further strengthened the revolt against vitalism.

Soon after the middle of last century it thus became a general belief among most biologists and numerous popular writers that life must ultimately be regarded as no more than a complicated physico-chemical process. In the writings of Huxley, for instance, we find this belief very clearly formulated. When, however, we attempt to form any detailed conception of what sort of physico-chemical process could, on the prevailing mechanistic conception of physics and chemistry, correspond with the characteristic features of life, the attempt breaks down completely. We can form no conception on these lines of how it is that a living organism, presuming it, as we must on the mechanistic theory, to be an extremely complex and delicately adjusted physico-chemical system, maintains and adjusts its characteristic form and activities in face of a varying environment, and reproduces them indefinitely often. This has already been made evident, and there is no need to enlarge upon it. Yet it seems impossible to return to vitalism, although in actual fact biologists have continued to use working hypotheses and modes of description which, if not vitalistic, are at any rate peculiar to biology.

Nevertheless a number of recent scientific investigators have adhered in essential respects to the conceptions represented in the writings of Stahl and the vitalists, or attempted, as Leibniz did, to give them a wider philosophical interpretation. The arguments of Driesch, based on his embryological investigations, may first be referred to. He proved clearly that each of the component cells of an early embryo is capable, after separation from the rest, of developing a complete embryo, and he interpreted this as due to the presence in each cell of an influence which he called 'entelechy', and regarded as being independent of environing conditions and determining the growth of an organism as an organic whole. It is certainly the case that from the standpoint of mechanistic principles we can form no idea of how it is that the capacity of reproducing an elaborate organism is handed down from cell to cell; but it may nevertheless be pointed out that the environment of a single cell is altered by its separation from other cells, so that in such a case as that which Driesch studied we have not eliminated the influence of environment. In this respect, therefore, his argument breaks down. The nature of each step in the growth of any part of an organism, as well as the cessation of growth at the adult stage, depends quite evidently on the environment of the part in question; and yet we cannot, from the mere standpoint of the physical sciences, see why it should be that the environment exerts on a living organism the characteristic integrating influence which it does exert.

In his book *The Interpretation of Development and Heredity* E. S. Russell has drawn conclusions essentially similar to those of Driesch, but from a wider embryological standpoint, and in his recently published *Modern Theories of Development* Bertalanaffy has focused the evidence for a somewhat similar view held by himself and many other embryologists. He distinguishes this, under the name of 'organismal' biology, from vitalism, since he regards the evident unity of life as inherent in living organisms, and not dependent on a separate influence. This avoids some of the difficulties and defects of vitalism. When one considers the nature of the facts which embryology discloses, and the failure of all attempts at a physico-chemical interpretation of these facts, it certainly seems at first sight as if we were driven back towards something like vitalism, under whatever name this fact may be disguised. Bergson's conception of the 'élan vital' is based mainly on the same class of facts.

From the standpoint of psychology MacDougall strongly supports animism, though he locates the interaction of body and mind, not in any one part of the brain or living body, but all over it. His conclusions are thus more nearly related to those of Stahl than to those of the later vitalists.

Leibniz (1646–1716) regarded the mind or soul as a self-determined 'monad', in which, however, the surrounding world is mirrored. It appeared to him that the universe consists of monads of different rank, God being the supreme monad. We might regard his philosophy as a very wide extension of animism. A recent philosophical writer who, following

Leibniz in essential points, but also basing his arguments on the newer conceptions of physical reality, has extended the conception of vitalism to the whole universe is Wildon Carr. Before his recent death he summarized his ideas in his book *Cogitans Cogitata*. He has resuscitated the idea of Leibniz that the universe consists of self-existent free monads, and extended this conception to atoms, electrons, and even photons as the simplest monads. But when we endeavour to understand how such independent monads could influence one another we encounter the difficulties which led Leibniz to the meaningless conception of a divinely pre-established harmony between the free inward activity of the monads and their apparent unco-ordinated influences on one another, dependent ultimately on mere abstract probability.

From the standpoint of philosophical physics Whitehead, particularly in his 'philosophy of organism', has pointed out identities between conceptions to which the new physical developments lead, and the phenomena presented in living organisms. General Smuts, in his book *Holism and Evolution*, has drawn similar conclusions from the biological side, emphasizing on the one hand the fact that the phenomena which occur in living organisms have the specific character of forming actively co-ordinated wholes, and, on the other, that even in inorganic phenomena similar actively co-ordinated wholes have been revealed by the newer physics. In his Presidential Address to the British Association (1931) he gave a summary of his reasoning, and particularly of its relations to the interpretation of evolution, which he regards as the unfolding of holistic reality in what had commonly been regarded as a purely mechanical universe.

While these writers point out clearly the difficulties in any mechanistic interpretation of life, or indeed of physical phenomena, they hardly deal satisfactorily with the difficulties which have already been pointed out in non-mechanistic conceptions of life. The fact that all the phenomena of life seem to depend ultimately on environing physical conditions led to the abandonment of vitalism, and this objection is not got rid of even if we extend what are essentially vitalistic conceptions so as to include phenomena met with in what has hitherto been regarded as the in-organic world. The essential difficulty seems to remain that the behaviour of a living organism depends ultimately on the unco-ordinated influence of a physical environment.

Let us, therefore, look more closely at the facts as observed. When we examine the characteristic features of life we find that, although every part and activity of a living organism, or of the environment connected with it, appears to be determined by its relations to other parts and activities, yet the deter-mination is normally so co-ordinated with the other parts and activities that the specific structure and activities of the organism tend to be maintained or reproduced. Though, therefore, there is constant activity or process in every part concerned, each activity or process, together with the normal structure, which is only an expression of this activity, tends to be maintained or reproduced in a certain specific manner. It seems evident, therefore, that in order to describe the phenomena we are compelled to assume that though any detail which we perceive may appear superficially to be an isolable physical or chemical phenomenon, yet the isolation is only apparent, and the phenomenon in reality involves the particular form of maintained co-ordination or integration which we call a life. By an artificial process of abstraction we can neglect the maintained co-ordination which we see, and this is what we do when we endeavour to interpret the phenomena physically or chemically. Nevertheless, what we actually see are living organisms living their own integrated lives. We require the word 'life' to designate this; and in biological science we use the word freely, though usually without a clear conception of what it implies.

In the development and maintenance of a living organism the co-ordination is very evident. The development of each part can be shown to be dependent on that of other parts and the environment; and the more closely development and maintenance are studied, the more evident does this become. But the particular manner in which the parts and environment influence one another is such that the specific structure and activities of the organism tend to be developed and maintained. They are unmistakably developed and maintained as a co-ordinated unity, and this is what we mean when we say that the organism lives a specific life.

The unity is thus actively and persistently present in each part and activity, including the influence of environment. The conception of an organism's life enables us to predict the maintenance and general behaviour of its parts and relations to environment so long as it lives, and in particular enables us to predict the general manner of its reproduction from a rudimentary part, in which the necessary genes are present, of the parent organism. This conception thus expresses a working hypothesis of the utmost value. In biology we are constantly looking for and finding the co-ordinated maintenance which we call life.

Life must thus be regarded as something which from the standpoint of biology is objectively real. We cannot describe it in terms of ordinary physical and chemical conceptions because these conceptions apply only to what we regard as isolable phenomena in both space and time, whereas the phenomena which we perceive as life are not isolable from one another, and can only be described as manifestations of the unity which we call life. The real basis of biology as a science is the conception of life, and apart from this conception biology would only be a chaotic collection of imperfectly defined physical and chemical observations—imperfectly defined because they do not express the co-ordinated maintenance.

According to ideas which are at present popular

the attribution of objective reality to life as such is an absurdity, since the only objective reality is physical reality. To those who reason in this manner I can only recommend a more careful consideration of the facts of ordinary observation with regard to life, and remind them at the same time that what they are basing their reasoning on is a fundamental philosophical assumption which, to me at least, appears inconsistent with actual experience.

When once we free ourselves from the entanglements of the mechanistic and vitalistic theories of life we can realize that the conception of life as maintained co-ordination gives us the working hypothesis which we are always in fact using in biology, though it may be without realizing it, and which sets no limits whatever to biological investigation, since there is no limit to the detail in which we discover co-ordinated maintenance.

The mere conception of life does not imply that of conscious behaviour, the discussion of which, and the respects in which it implies much more than life, will be taken up in the next chapter. The phenomena of life are regarded as occurring blindly, without foresight or retrospect, and merely as co-ordinated maintenance or reproduction of a specific life. This co-ordinated maintenance implies continuous adaptation to changing circumstances, and where we meet with specially striking instances of adaptation we may be inclined to interpret the adaptation as guided by conscious foresight; but there is usually little difficulty in distinguishing actual foresight from cases which we can interpret as being nothing more than blind adaptation. Conscious behaviour is much more than what we regard as mere life.

When we look only at the immediate details of what is present or happening in a living organism we seem everywhere to find processes which we imagine to be either capable of being actually described in terms of physical science, or to give promise of becoming capable in future of such description. Yet all these processes are in actual fact co-ordinated in such a manner that the organism tends to maintain or reproduce what is characteristic of its life, and it is this co-ordinated maintenance that we call life.

We can take as an example the blood circulation. The detailed investigations of Harvey and his successors might seem on superficial examination to show that the blood is simply pumped round mechanically by the action of the heart. But it has also been shown, and continues to be further shown in greater and greater detail, that the circulation is everywhere co-ordinated locally and generally with the maintenance in structure and activity of each part of the body, so that the blood propelled by each beat of the heart, as well as the frequency of beat, is determined in this way. Special stimuli or inhibitions, acting locally, are such as to bring this about, and it is the requirements of the tissues, and not primarily the action of the heart, which determine the rate of circulation through each part.

We might still endeavour to represent blood circulation as the result of an elaborate system of machinery, and since the middle of last century it has been commonly represented in this way. But the heart, blood, and all the amazingly delicate details of blood-vessels, associated nervous system, and their behaviour, have developed from an embryo showing no such structure, and are actively maintained as 'normal' structures acting normally. The machine theory, however useful it is up to a certain point, gives no account of this, and of the similar phenomena which are met with everywhere in the bodies of living organisms. In my book *Respiration* I have shown how co-ordinated maintenance enters into all respiratory activity.[1]

Vitalism was a quite insufficiently thorough attempt to take the co-ordinated maintenance into account. It was unsuccessful for the reasons already stated, but its failure leaves the facts just as they were. Except quite superficially, the phenomena observed in the lives of organisms cannot be interpreted as mere physical and chemical processes, at least in the sense of the current Newtonian physical conceptions. The latter processes are interpreted as separable events in separable units of material, and in consequence of this the quite evidently maintained co-ordination or wholeness of life cannot be expressed in terms of them.

[1] A new edition of this book, by Dr. J. G. Priestley and myself, has just been published by the Clarendon Press.

When we consider the matter carefully we can see that in the question as to the nature of life the ultimate validity of the whole physical and chemical conception of the universe is involved. No one could question the practical usefulness of the latter conception; but its ultimate validity is another matter. The vitalists did not question its ultimate validity with respect to what is outside living organisms, but maintained that inside living organisms something interferes with its validity. It appears clearly to me that what made their position untenable was the fact that, following the trend of their times, they accepted the ultimate validity of physical and chemical interpretation outside the bodies of 'living' organisms. Once this is admitted, we find that we are driven to admit also that life must be regarded as a physical and chemical process. But this brings us back again to the incoherencies already pointed out.

The mistake of the vitalists was, as I have repeatedly tried to point out in previous writings, to separate the conception of a living organism from that of its environment. The maintained co-ordination is present, just as much in the relations between organism and environment as in the relations between the parts of an organism itself. It does not seem to me that in the 'organismal', 'organicist', or 'holistic' conceptions of life the mistake of vitalism has been at all completely avoided, since organisms are regarded apart from their environment. Life thus appears, just as for vitalism, to be no more than a mysterious accident in a physical universe. We cannot separate in space the phenomena of life from those of its environment.

This statement raises in a direct manner a far-reaching question as to the relationship between biological and physical interpretation of our experience. It is mainly through our senses that we are in relation with our external environment; and hitherto it has been very usually assumed, in at least modern times, that, apart from general philosophical questions such as those discussed in Chapter I, the environment of a living organism can be regarded as a physical environment to which the sense-organs respond passively. In examining this assumption we may take as an example the case of vision. In vision we become aware of differences in brightness and in colour of what we see around us, including their localization, and our visual experience is, apart from the psychological interpretation of it, which will be discussed in the next chapter, entirely based on differences in brightness and colour and their localization.

We can consider sensory phenomena of brightness and colour, or any other sensory phenomena, as mere physiological responses, apart from the interpretations involved in them as perceived objects. Scientific treatment of them under this limitation belongs to physiology, not psychology, so that the physiology of the senses as studied by conscious responses to sensory stimuli is an important part of physiology, in spite of the fact that we may be conscious of these responses.

We can study them physiologically, just as we study breathing or nutrition, in spite of our being conscious of them, and in spite of all that this implies, as discussed in the next chapter. We are disregarding, or abstracting from, the psychological aspects of our experience, as defined in the next chapter.

If we neglect the study in ourselves of physiological processes, regardless of our being conscious of them, we are neglecting a most important field of physiological observation. My own work as a physiologist has been very largely in connexion with phenomena, such as breathing, of which we are fully conscious.

We may first discuss differences in brightness.[1] We have become accustomed to assume that they are simply due to differences in the intensity of light coming to us from a surrounding physical world. But when we examine this conception physiologically we find that it is only under certain definite physiological conditions that the brightness of an area in the visual field corresponds with what we regard as intensity of objective illumination. If we keep the total illumination of the visual field constant, as is for instance the case in ordinary steady good daylight or artificial illumination, the brightnesses of small parts of it can be shown experimentally to correspond to

[1] An account of experimental demonstrations of the argument in the succeeding paragraphs will be found in papers by me in the *Journal of Physiology*, vol. lxxix, p. 121, 1933, and the *British Medical Journal*, 23 December 1933.

what we regard as intensities of the light transmitted from them; but this is not the case at all if we vary the general illumination, since we can increase or diminish the illumination within wide limits without, except for a very short time, increasing or diminishing sensibly the brightness of an object seen. If, however, the object seen is separately illuminated, then increase in illumination of the surrounding field makes it darker, and may make it completely black, while diminution in illumination of the surrounding field increases correspondingly its brightness.

It is thus on contrast that the visibility of brightness and darkness depends; and this fact is known as an example of Weber's or Fechner's general law of response to sensory stimuli. Looking at the matter from a rather different standpoint, we can say that the brightness of an object in the visual field remains the same over wide differences in illumination, but that if one part of the field is illuminated more brightly or less brightly, a corresponding other part will appear less bright or more bright than before.

When the general illumination becomes very small this generalization seems at first sight to hold no longer, and we are apt to imagine that in what we regard as complete darkness our whole field of vision is correspondingly dark. Weber's law in its crude form ceases to hold good in dim light. When, however, we observe more closely, we find that in what we regard as absolute darkness the visual field is not black, but lit up by what is known to physiologists as the 'intrinsic' illumination, in which we see small evanescent areas of brightness and darkness, neutral in colour, and giving the general impression of grey. The brightness in the intrinsic illumination is relative to the darkness, just as when we see objects around us. In what we regard as very dim light the differences in objective illumination are in reality partly obscured by the intrinsic illumination, and are thus no longer visible clearly. On going into very dim light we at first cannot see things at all clearly, but after a time, which may be as long as half an hour, we are able to see them easily. Our sight is 'adapted' to the dim light. What really happens is that the intrinsic illumination is at first strong, and covers up the objective illumination. This is because after-effects of previous illumination add themselves at first to the intrinsic illumination.

By means of a photometer we can measure what we interpret as objective degrees of illumination. These are relative to the illumination given by a standard source of light—a standard candle, other flame-lamp, or electric lamp—at a certain distance. We express these degrees of illumination as foot-candles or metre-candles. But in all cases the actual estimations are made in the same evenly distributed surrounding and environing illumination or darkness, and it is only the equality of brightness when a reading is made that we have actually attended to : not absolute brightness, since this varies with different environing conditions, and therefore with any differences which exist in the brightnesses which we are comparing. Brightness is meaningless apart from contrast. There is, in fact, no such thing as a merely objective cause of brightness in a physical sense, though we obtain a measurement which we can artificially interpret physically as if there were; and in this artificial sense we can extend indefinitely our measurements or estimations of brightness, and relate observations of brightness with various independent physically interpreted measurements.

When we regard the phenomena of brightness and darkness from a physiological standpoint the fact stands out clearly that not only are they meaningless apart from one another, but that a balance between them tends to be maintained in the field of vision, however much what we interpret as the objective illumination may vary. This is the physiological significance of Weber's law when we remodel it so that it can cover the phenomena of vision in all fields of illumination, including intrinsic illumination. In visual activity we thus find a form of specific maintenance which has the same character as other specific features of life, and in interpreting the visual relations between organisms and environment as regards degrees of brightness we must apply the same general conception as we apply with regard to the mutual relations between the parts themselves of an organism, including their immediate environments. Our experiences of degrees of brightness are thus experiences of life itself, and cannot be interpreted in terms of the conception that they merely express the result of action upon us of changes in a physically interpreted environment. When we describe them as experiences of objective brightness or illumination existing independently of experience of them, we are only applying a convenient hypothesis or artifice, which is far from completely expressing the observed facts, but which enables us to relate visual experiences to other experiences of what we interpret as an objective physical world.

Let us now consider differences in colour. In our visual field we see many different varieties of colour, and it has become natural to us to attribute these differences simply to the differences in physical quality of the light which reaches us, our eyes being passive in this process. In accordance with the discoveries of Newton and his successors, light which we regard as white is also to be regarded as a balanced mixture of lights of differing wave-lengths or refrangibilities; and to each wave-length a corresponding experience of colour is assumed to correspond. On pigmented surfaces light of certain wave-lengths is absorbed preferentially, leaving a mixture to be reflected which gives the corresponding colour; and on dark surfaces most of the light of all sorts is absorbed.

Under certain conditions this theory of colour vision answers to our experience of colour, just as under certain conditions our experience of brightness answers to the corresponding theory that brightness depends on the strength of a light stimulus. We can show easily, however, that the theory is inadequate.

It is known to many persons that if we throw on a white surface two shadows of an upright bar, such as a pencil, one shadow being produced by a candle or ordinary electric lamp, and the other by a chink of daylight, the shadow thrown by the candle, if it is neither too near nor too far away, will be deep blue, and that thrown by the daylight deep orange-yellow. One shadow is evidently lit by the daylight alone, and the other by the candle alone. We might imagine, as did Helmholtz, that the daylight shadow is yellow because candlelight is orange-yellow, and the other appears to be the complementary colour blue through a natural error of judgement. But whether we see the yellow shadow or block it out by placing a black object over it, the other shadow appears blue. Moreover, the white surface looks white with either the daylight alone, or the candlelight alone, or with both lights together. Thus no distinctively psychological explanation is possible. The treatment of colour contrast and other contrast phenomena by Helmholtz and Fechner has had a most unfortunate influence on both the physiology of the senses and psychology.

We can vary the experiment by using coloured electric lamps, or coloured glasses in front of a candle, in place of the daylight. The effects will probably seem very extraordinary. With a bluish-green lamp the shadow lit by the candle becomes red : with a red lamp it becomes green : with an orange-yellow lamp it becomes blue : and with a lemon-yellow lamp violet. We can in fact make the shadow lit by the candle any colour of the spectrum we please. Moreover, we get a similar result if, in place of the light from a candle or uncoloured electric lamp, we use the almost pure spectral light of a sodium flame. What is equally re-markable is that with all the changing mixtures of light the screen itself appears white or nearly so.

We are accustomed to use the word 'contrast' in connexion with the influence of one colour on the appearance of an adjoining one. But in this case the contrast, if we can call it so, is between the apparently white surface and a shadow illuminated by a slightly different quality of light, the result being that this difference is greatly increased or quite distorted. How, moreover, are we to account for the screen or white surface continuing to look white, in spite of the differences in the quality of the light reflected from it ? The screen looks white, in spite of what is physically speaking a marked difference in quality of the light illuminating it. The same point can be illustrated in a striking manner with a piece of transparent coloured tissue giving a not too deep blue or other colour when placed on a white surface. On raising this to the eyes, so that it wholly covers the field of vision, the white surface appears again white.

We can apparently get rid of contrast by looking at homogeneously coloured objects with one eye through a narrow tube made of dull black paper, or lined with black velvet, to stop reflection of light.

A tube about a foot long and half an inch wide is suitable. When we look in this way at a coloured shadow, the characteristic colour disappears, but other unexpected colours are seen. The blue shadow illuminated by daylight, or indeed any white surface illuminated by daylight or ordinary electric light, becomes distinctly yellow, and the variously coloured shadows illuminated by the candle or electric lamp, or any white surface illuminated by them, become still more markedly yellow. What is much more surprising is that even when for ordinary vision the clear sky, or the sea, appears deep blue, it rapidly becomes pure white, though with some persons only nearly so, when looked at through the tube. The blue reappears again at once, however, if a cloud is allowed to pass into the field of vision. The blueness of the sky is thus a 'contrast' blueness. All isolated colours which we look at through a black tube are twisted round towards orange-yellow, though this is much more marked with the complementary colour blue. Through a blackened tube, when contrast is excluded, all the gorgeous blues, greens, pinks, and purples which we see in the sky, sea, and hills melt away into white or shades of orange-yellow, in so far as they are not due to pigmentation.

The colour effects which we get with a blackened tube are similar to those when we look at illuminated objects in surrounding darkness. For instance, the white surfaces in a house lit by electric or flame-lamps look yellow as we approach or first enter it from darkness outside, and a sufficiently small piece of white surface illuminated by diffused daylight in a darkened visual field becomes distinctly yellow.

In complete external darkness the field of vision is not black, but, as already mentioned, lit up by the intrinsic illumination, which has a general neutral grey colour when it is not disturbed by the after-effects which soon subside. It is apparently this which gives us a standard of white to which no ordinary artificial light, and not even noonday diffused daylight in, at any rate, non-tropical countries, conforms. It is also with reference to this standard, when it prevails over almost the whole of the field of vision, that we see colours of all kinds as they appear through a blackened tube, or in surrounding darkness. Hence by blotting out surrounding visible objects from our field of vision we do not get rid of colour contrast, but only alter its nature, so that, for instance, a pigmented surface which is ordinarily blue becomes white if the blue is not too brilliant.

The neutral grey of intrinsic illumination appears to be identical in tint with that of a white or grey surface illuminated solely by direct sunlight while the sun is high and the sky clear. It is as if the intrinsic illumination were a piece of sunlit unpigmented surface which was always available as a standard for comparison, and was called into use by employing a blackened tube. Not all persons, however, seem to have quite the same standard of white.

Striking examples of 'contrast' effects have just been

given, but one characteristic of coloured shadows has not been remarked on. It is that the colours of the two shadows are complementary. That is to say that when they are superposed they give the white colour of the background, as is shown by the fact that when by removing the upright bar we add to the illumination of either shadow the illumination which was present in the other shadow, the corresponding part of the background is white. Another very significant fact is that in these experiments the screen continues to look white, although by other tests, as when we look at it through a blackened tube, it may appear yellow or some other colour. It is evident that it appears white in virtue of active physiological effort, just as the standard of white given by the intrinsic illumination embodies evident physiological activity. The active effort is towards the co-ordinated balance of complementary colour which we call white, and in the complementary colours seen in coloured shadows we find a realization of the same balance. We notice also that these colours blend harmoniously in the field of vision. They carry with them emotional satisfaction in a manner that other juxtapositions of two colours do not.

Since our experience of white, and with it black, embodies physiological activity, it follows that all the colours we see, since they are referred to what appears white, embody physiological activity whether or not they are accompanied by mutual contrast effects. But this is what we mean when we regard them all as dependent on contrast. As white signifies a neutral balance of other colours, the activity is in the direction of producing such a balance. It does not matter whether the balance is produced by what can be regarded as a superposition or as a juxtaposition of complementary colours. In the coloured shadows we make complementary colours just as we make the neutral white background of superposed complementary colours.

Although contrast between different colours, when it exists, is a very striking fact, yet we commonly see different colours in juxtaposition to one another without any mutual contrast effect being appreciable, just as we commonly see arithmetical differences in brightness without any mutual contrast effects between them. The reason for this is of the same nature in both cases. It is when the general brightness of the visual field remains almost uniform that we see separable arithmetical differences in brightness; and similarly it is when the general brightness of the visual field is almost uniform that we see separable or arithmetical differences in colour without mutual contrast. These are referred to the general colour as a constant standard, though this standard, as already shown, is always a physiological one. When, however, the brightness varies considerably in any part of the visual field, contrast effects in the less intensely illuminated parts become very appreciable, and are familiar to artists in the painting of shadows. The coloured shadows already described are examples of this. They are essentially shadows, and when an experimental arrangement is employed which makes it possible to vary the intensity of the illumination of a shaded area emitting light of different quality, without varying the general illumination of the visual field, the contrast effect on this shaded area varies inversely with its illumination, and disappears when the formerly shaded area becomes as bright as the screen itself.

The reason why contrast effects become visible on shadows or dimly illuminated areas is that while the feeble illumination has little appreciable influence on the general balance of the colours seen, this balance has a great influence on vision of the colour in the shaded area. What we see as blue sky, for instance, is feebly illuminated as compared with clouds, haze, &c., in the field of vision around it. The feeble light coming to us directly from clear sky above has lost proportionately less of its violet and blue by scattering than the much stronger light coming to us obliquely from the sun, and reflected from or coming through clouds and haze. But our standard of whiteness is actively made to correspond with the prevailing light. Hence the clear sky above looks blue, while the clouds, &c., are not appreciably yellow, though if their light is not too bright or the surface looked at too large the yellow becomes evident through a blackened tube, for the reasons already given. The blueness of the sky or sea is essentially that of a coloured shadow, in which we cannot distinguish what is objective from what is subjective.

The response to a visual stimulus differs according as the stimulus is localized and extended in the visual field. The stimulus is said to have a 'local sign', and this is so whether or not the rest of the field is externally illuminated. What this means is that the rest of the field is actively present always, and that the stimulus exists in relation to it. Maintenance of an extended field is thus involved in the localization and extension of visual stimuli, just as maintenance of brightness and colour is involved in the vision of brightness and colour. In responses to localization and extension we are thus also dealing with what is characteristic of life.

Looking back at what has been said as to vision of the localized brightness and colour which fills our visual field, we can see that it is impossible to distinguish in them what is 'objective' from what is 'subjective', or dependent on ourselves. But this merely negative fact is by no means all. Throughout our world of vision we can everywhere trace the active maintenance of a co-ordinated balance of brightness and darkness, and of colour and complementary colour, together with a maintained field of vision, each part of which exists only in co-ordination with the other parts. As already pointed out, this co-ordinated maintenance is the characteristic mark of life, so that the conception of life is essential in the scientific interpretation of our universe as we see it. If we dispense with this conception we are left with all the unintelligible facts which the phenomena of 'contrast' and localization would now present. From lack of any sufficient appreciation of the significance of contrast and localization, physiologists, since the times of Galileo and Newton, have been content to accept as sufficient the purely physical conception of a surrounding visible universe. Kant did so also in his account of the 'phenomenal' world in his first *Critique*, and we find the same thing in what is at present the popular identification of physically interpreted reality with something which is quite independent of our perception of it, so that we are no more than 'observers' of what is entirely independent of us. When we realize, for example, that in our 'observing' the blue sky we are also making it blue, our attitude to the 'nature' which we see around us becomes very different.

Perhaps the first impression produced by realization that the world of localized brightness and colour which we see around us cannot be regarded as 'objective' or independent of our own physiological activity is one of scepticism or else of disappointment. We perhaps think that the phenomena which apparently prove this conclusion are psychological illusions, or else that we have lost something which we had depended on. But when we realize, as a good artist does in practice, that in what we see around us, we ourselves are always present, and we are not mere 'observers' of what is outside us, our visual environment becomes in reality not merely something much nearer to truth, but of far greater personal interest.

The oppression produced by the idea of a perceived world in which we have no part disappears. We have found ourselves in this perceived world, and in no mere generalized philosophical sense such as Kant pointed out, but in a much more concrete sense related to ourselves as individuals. In the succeeding chapters, however, this line of reasoning will be carried much further.

The sense of touch or pressure, with its localization, represents what is still more fundamental than vision, but similar considerations apply to it as to vision. Vision itself may indeed be regarded as nothing more than a special modification of touch, so that the field of vision is fundamentally the same as the field of touch. The existence of contrast, involving Weber's law, is just as evident in the case of touch or pressure as in vision. And just as there is intrinsic illumination in vision, so there is what may be called intrinsic sense of touch, and a threshold beneath which Weber's law in its crude form entirely ceases to apply. Thus there is a constantly maintained field of touch, which in its turn gives significance at all times to localization of touch.

Hence the organic maintenance which is characteristic of life is involved just as much in the sense of touch as in vision. The sense-data of touch are definitely localized in three dimensions, and it seems to be mainly through the underlying identity in the fields of touch and vision that localization of visual sense-data is tridimensional.

On considéring other senses than that of vision or touch we can see that similar reasoning applies to them also. It is, for instance, in our sense of effort that we experience what we call inertia and the force required to overcome it. But Weber's law applies to sense of effort just as much as to vision, so that contrast is just as real, and we can give to it the same interpretation as with vision and touch. Sense of effort may indeed be regarded as a variety of sense of touch, applying to parts specially connected with contracting muscles. Just as in the case of vision of brightness, we form and extend indefinitely an artificial arithmetical scale of inertia or mass. We can regard this scale as objective, but it has no concrete existence apart from our experience of the masses we directly perceive the resistance of, such as grammes or pounds. These are our real standards, though as representing a perceived standard of effort they only remain constant in so far as our experience of them occurs under certain definite physiological conditions. By altering these conditions we can alter the standards, but the fact of their forming new standards of contrast is a manifestation of maintained life. In this respect the standards of inertia or mass are like standards of brightness. We refer experiences of mass and illumination to standards which represent sense experiences under constant physiological conditions, but in treating them as mass and illumination in a physical sense we neglect this fact.

It is the same with other physical observations.

Our lives are present in them: we are not mere observers of what is outside of us, any more than we are mere observers when we see the lights and colours of the sky. A mere observer is only a convenient figment. Our own sense-experiences as expressions of life are embodied in all we perceive, though what we perceive embodies much more than what can be interpreted biologically, as will appear in the following chapter.

Apart from visible, tangible, or otherwise sensible standards of length, mass, and time, our universe becomes an unreal one of abstract mathematical relations divorced from actuality. We can alter as much as we please the actual units in which we express length, mass, time, and all that depends on them, provided that any new unit can be expressed in terms of sensible units such as centimetres, grammes, or seconds. Abstract mathematical science enables us to do this. But the ultimate basis of physical measurement is always a sensible unit, the sensible constancy of which depends on the maintained constancy of the physiological conditions under which it is experienced.

The fact that we cannot separate what is objective from what is subjective in our sense-experience carries with it much else. Sense-experiences are stimuli to specific action or rest. They thus enter into the general life of any organism which they are present to; and when we consider the manner of this entry we find that they are playing a part in the maintenance of the organism's life. They are guiding the actions which sum themselves up in this maintenance or the maintenance of the organism's race. The various emotional instinctive or reflex accompaniments, or tropisms, which belong to sensory experiences interpret themselves in this way.

In his account of physiological responses to sensory impressions Descartes, as already mentioned, represented each response as due to an impulse reaching a certain portion of the brain, and there liberating a further influence leading to contraction of a certain muscle or group of muscles. Thus the response is due fundamentally to what is called reflex action. This physical conception of the response is, however, insufficient for the reason that the actual response depends always on the surrounding physiological conditions. These determine both the nature and strength of the response, or whether any response at all occurs. Taking the responses as a whole, moreover, they are such as express maintenance of the co-ordinated unity which we call the life of the organism. But this co-ordinated unity cannot be expressed in physical terms, so that the physical conception of response to a sensory impulse is insufficient, and we must substitute a biological conception based on the fact that in physiological stimuli and responses there is an expression of life. As has just been shown, sensory stimuli, even when taken by themselves without reference to muscular responses to them, must be regarded as expressions of life.

When we also take into consideration the muscular and other responses to them the same inference applies, but in a wider sense. The fact that for any living organism the nature of its environment is determined by its own particular life was pointed out strikingly by von Uexküll in his book *Umwelt und Innenwelt der Tiere*.

We can neglect the biological aspects of sensory experiences, and we do so in physical interpretation. This is, however, a mere matter of practical convenience in certain limited connexions. For biological interpretation these limitations are not present. Although physical science rests ultimately on sense-experience, yet in so far as physical science does not take account of more than a limited portion of what is involved in sense-experience it is an abstract science. By its abstractness it can extend immensely the scope of its application, but the application deals only with a limited and artificial aspect of experience.

Let us endeavour to define more closely the difference between physical and biological interpretation. From the standpoint of the traditional physical sciences a living organism and its environment appear as a complex aggregation of separable units of matter associated causally with one another in separable events. From the biological standpoint, on the other hand, the apparently separable units of matter and events are seen not to be actually separable, but, in their relationships with one another, to be taking part in the manifestation of the co-ordinated and persistent whole which is called life, and which has no definite limits either spatially or temporally. Thus the separable units and events of physical interpretation are seen to be indefinite.

An example will perhaps make this statement more clear. From the standpoint of physical science we seem to be able to trace the course of oxygen atoms into living substance, and their course out again; but how they are determined in their course remains altogether obscure. From the standpoint of biology, however, their presence and behaviour at any point relative to other points in the living body are no longer what we can regard as separable events, but an expression of an organism's life. As mere separable events they are imperfectly defined, whereas as an expression of an organism's life they become to this extent intelligible and predictable, since they express the maintained co-ordination which we recognize as that of a life. This maintained co-ordination becomes, of course, meaningless as soon as we make the vain attempt to resolve it into nothing but separable units of matter and events. It is the maintenance of co-ordination which we are always considering in biology.

The reality of the atoms and their movements appears under a new aspect owing to the co-ordinated maintenance which they display, and which illuminates what is otherwise the unintelligibility of their characteristic presence and behaviour. We must regard life, not, with vitalism, as something projected into an otherwise physically interpretable universe, but as this universe itself interpreted more adequately, the more adequate interpretations showing itself in the phenomena which we recognize as characteristic of life. If we assume that self-existent matter and its motions represent reality, a universe which includes life is unintelligible. The fact of life shows that the self-existence postulated by physical interpretation is only an imperfect appearance. The oxygen atoms and their behaviour are for biology the expression of an organism's life, and what we might regard as only our partial physical and chemical knowledge regarding them becomes an expression of the maintenance of the organism's life.

The scientific and practical use of physical and chemical conceptions is evident, since they enable us to predict an immense variety of what we call inorganic phenomena with great success. It may be asked what corresponding use attaches to the conception of life. The answer is that where what we call life is concerned the conception of its existence in the sense already explained enables us to predict successfully in a manner not otherwise possible. We are apt, in biology, to take for granted the existence of life without realizing what we are taking for granted. We accept as fact that any kind of living organism is developed and maintained throughout an extraordinarily characteristic life-history, and is reproduced with accuracy in its descendants, so that one species is sharply distinguished from another.

Physics and chemistry afford no theoretical account of all this, but the conception of life does.

As soon as we recognize that any detail of either structure or activity belongs to the life of an organism we know that this detail is no mere fleeting phenomenon, but an expression of what tends to be maintained as an expression of the organism's life. What biology on either its morphological or physiological side is always looking for is evidence that details are real expressions of maintained life, and in what exact respect. The whole of morphological and physiological knowledge constitutes therefore, however little this may be realized, a justification for employing the conception of life as the working hypothesis of biology.

Without the conception of life as such, even though this conception may have been used by mere implication, biology would be no science at all, but only a chaotic collection of imperfectly defined physical and chemical data. Vitalism in its various forms gave no effective help of a positive character, since it excluded from its purview the environment of an organism. The unity of life extends over the environment of an organism no less than over its own body, and the vitalists failed to recognize this fact, with disastrous results for their theory, and much confusion in biology itself.

We might suppose that if we could put together in its ordinary environment all the atoms and molecules in their proper arrangement which we picture as existing at any time in a living organism we should have the living organism itself. But life involves active maintenance and power of indefinitely repeated reproduction. There would be nothing to represent this in the body artificially produced from atoms and molecules as ordinarily conceived. It would therefore not be alive, but a mere unstable artefact, with only a temporary superficial resemblance to life. A living organism cannot be put together, since maintenance is of its essence; it therefore has a continuous history and grows from what is already alive. Life as such is an objective reality, and no artefact which can be put together out of separable parts.

Physical science, even in its quite modern form, does not take account of the co-ordinated maintenance which is present in the world of our actual experience. It would perhaps be more correct to say that it now does so to some extent in the conceptions which are being applied to the behaviour of very minute physically interpreted entities, such as atoms, electrons, or photons. In this development we can see indications of a less abstract attitude in physical science. We find also a practical recognition in recent physics of the fact that in the observation of certain phenomena we are at the same time making them.

In our interpretation of experience as experience of lives, including our own lives, we are evidently seeing less incompletely than in mere physical interpretation. Lives are there in nature, and in any general interpretation of nature we cannot disregard them any more

than we can disregard chemical or electrical phenomena or the phenomena of radiation. But when we
take life into consideration it gives us a deeper insight
into what we may have previously set down as
capable of mere physical interpretation.

Biological interpretation covers the whole of our
perceived universe in so far as we leave conscious
behaviour out of account. On this point we must
definitely break with any philosophy which, in the
manner of vitalism, interprets our universe of experience as made up of a scattered picture in which we
find here what is purely physical, there what is biological, and there what is spiritual. Physical interpretation, in so far as we adhere to it, is applicable to the
whole of our perceived experience. But so is biological interpretation, and so, as will be shown in the
next chapter, is psychological interpretation. At each
level of interpretation the whole of our experience is
covered. Inasmuch, however, as in biological interpretation we are taking our experience more fully into
account than in physical interpretation, biological
interpretation is on a higher level, and represents
reality less incompletely than physical interpretation.

The fact that the life of an organism extends over
its environment implies that the lives of different
organisms, although they are distinguishable, enter
into each other's lives. There is no spatial separation
between the lives of different organisms, just as there
is no spatial separation within the life of any one
organism. But the part played by the life of one

organism in the life of a second is, from a mere biological standpoint, only intelligible as entering into
the life of the second. For biology the universe
appears as a universe of individual lives, each of
which can be regarded separately, though it may
enter into the lives of other organisms.

There is no real inconsistency between physical and
biological interpretation, provided that we realize
that the latter represents deeper insight or fuller perception. As regards life, therefore, Kant was mistaken in separating a phenomenal world of perception
from an unperceivable world of aesthetic judgement.
He was misled by the rigid character of his interpretation of perception, and his mistake is constantly being
repeated in present-day science and literature. Life is
just as much an object of ordinary perception as is
mechanism, and belongs just as much to our 'common-sense' world, inconsistent with itself as that
world is. We have just as good a right to consider the
biologically interpreted world to be a directly perceived world of common sense as we have to consider
the physically interpreted world in this manner, and
biologists, albeit unconsciously, are constantly making use of biological common sense.

What we interpret biologically is the same perceived world as we can also, if we look, as Descartes
and Kant did, less closely, endeavour to interpret
physically; and biological perception or interpretation may seem to be only physical perception or interpretation carried further. In reality, however, the

two sorts of interpretation are different. Biological interpretation may be said to be forced on us through the failure of physical interpretation; but from another standpoint what we are seeking after in biology is from the outset no mere physical interpretation, since the nature of what we discover in biology is incapable of being expressed in physical terms. Physical interpretation in its ordinary sense is in terms of existences and events which can be distinguished as separable from other existences and events, while biological interpretation is in terms of what is not thus separable, but is regarded as belonging essentially to the co-ordinated and persistent existence which we call the life of an organism. When we find that any detail of structure or activity enters into the co-ordinated and persistent life of an organism we have reached the biological interpretation or perception of this detail; and it is this kind of interpretation that biological science seeks.

Let us take an illustration of this from physiology. From a physical and chemical standpoint we can estimate what substances enter the body through the mouth and lungs, and what substances leave it through the kidneys and lungs and skin, or in the faeces. But this does not tell us how the apparent flow of material through the body results in the maintenance of its structure and activities : nor is there the smallest reason for believing that however far we carry physical or chemical investigation we shall get any nearer to understanding this fact. We do understand it, however, in so far as we can show by experiment that the apparent flow of material is an expression of the life of an organism, regarding its life as an objective reality which we are investigating all the time, and of which we verify the existence in discovering how the phenomena participate in the maintenance of the organism's life and in its reproduction.

From the standpoint of the general principle of relativity every element in the universe of our experience has its existence in its relations to other elements. From the biological standpoint also each phenomenon in the life of an organism has its existence in relation to the other phenomena of its life. But in biology we are in presence of the fact that the phenomena so related are co-ordinated and maintained in specific relationships, thus constituting the individual lives of organisms, and so giving them objective reality as phenomena of life. We may thus say that in biology the principle of relativity is carried much further than in relativity physics, and so becomes the basis of biology, a science which describes reality more fundamentally than does physical science. From the standpoint of the new physics there seems to be no difficulty in regarding biological interpretation as a less incomplete form of interpretation than mere physical interpretation. Both the structure and activities observed in the bodies of living organisms, and their environments in so far as they enter into their lives, embody, from the biological standpoint, their actively maintained relationships to one another, and the physical conception of unco-ordinated inertia is replaced by the biological conception of specific maintenance of co-ordinated life.

Whatever ideas we may form of matter, its reality seems to be mainly expressed in our idea of its inertia or mass—the persistency of its passive existence. In our conception of life the idea of persistence becomes that of persistence in its co-ordinated activity. What we call mass in the physically interpreted world becomes in biology persistent life with constant adaptation, and the physical units of the physical world become units in a biological sense for biological interpretation, though we do not yet see clearly how to interpret biologically what we are accustomed to consider physical units such as atoms. We can look on the life of a higher organism as a unity of the passing lives of its constituent cells, but we do not yet see how to interpret the life of a cell as a unity of the passing lives of what we at present know as atoms, electrons, or protons.

From the physical standpoint biological phenomena are indefinitely complex, and for this practical reason alone are incapable of being formulated in physical form, and thus remain unintelligible; but they are also unintelligible in the deeper sense that they are essentially undefinable physically. From the biological standpoint, however, they are intelligible through the perception that they are maintained or reproduced in a characteristic manner. Life is from its very nature incapable of being described or understood in terms of mere physical conceptions. It is not biology, but physics, that from the biological standpoint is an 'inexact' science. Biological explanation or description is essentially different from physical explanation or description, and aims at the discovery by observation and experiment of specific maintained relationships in phenomena, the existence of which makes prediction possible.

It has often been asked whether the existence of life involves a creation or disappearance of energy; and when we consider how remarkable many physiological reactions appear to be, it might appear as if they involved either a creation or annihilation of what, from the physical standpoint, we interpret as energy. But a little consideration shows us that in putting such a question we are attempting, like the vitalists, to apply physical and biological conceptions simultaneously. For biological interpretation the physical conception of energy has lost its meaning, since the environment of an organism is no longer regarded as a physical environment. We cannot separate physiological stimulus and response in the same way as we distinguish transfers and liberations of energy in a physical sense: the reason being that the activity represented in both stimulus and response is part of an organism's co-ordinated life, and cannot be described or expressed as separable events. The question thus becomes meaningless because it involves a presupposition which is meaningless for biology; and for physics it does not admit of any definite investigation, owing to the apparent endless complexity of the phenomena.

We can investigate in the most minute and thorough manner what appear to us to be the physical and chemical phenomena involved in life, and there is no limit to the discoveries which could be included under the general headings of 'biophysics' or 'biochemistry'. But when we put these discoveries together as mere physics and chemistry they are always indefinite, since they do not tell anything about the fact that the phenomena they refer to are co-ordinated and maintained. The more of such discoveries are made the more amazing and unintelligible from a physical and chemical standpoint do the co-ordination, maintenance, and reproduction become. We come to realize, moreover, that apart from their co-ordination and maintenance biophysical and biochemical phenomena are devoid of interest to biologists. It is the fact of their co-ordination and maintenance as manifestations of life that gives them their significance.

In so far as this is so it is misleading to call their study biophysics or biochemistry. They are in reality biology, and embody distinctively biological conceptions. If we called them physical or chemical physiology these designations would no longer be misleading, though the separation of a physical from a chemical side of physiology is no more than a matter of practical convenience, dependent on the fact that some physiologists are more familiar with physical, and others with chemical apparatus and methods.

It is commonly argued that if we accept completely the fact of evolution, we have also accepted the conclusion that life has in some way arisen out of conditions which can be described completely in traditional physical and chemical terms. Thus, though we cannot at present understand how such a phenomenon as life could originate out of such conditions, and the attempts hitherto made to make the origination intelligible have been simply childish, we must nevertheless assume that there has been such an origination.

We need, however, make no such unintelligible assumption; for we are free to conclude that when we examine more completely what we at present call the inorganic world we shall find in it phenomena which are the same as those of life. Until about twenty-five years ago this conclusion seemed inconsistent with current physical and chemical conceptions. It was only a philosophical faith such as I had myself at that time expressed. But recent advances in physics have brought us much nearer to such a conclusion. An atom, or even an electron, or light-quantum, is for recent physics something of which the existence, like that of a living organism, is an expression of ceaseless co-ordinated activity, incapable of being interpreted in mechanical terms as that of a mere particle in the old sense. We even find Planck, the originator of one of the great new directions of discovery in physics, concluding that 'the assumption that the orderly course of a process can be represented by an analysis of it into temporal and spatial processes must be dropped. The conception of wholeness must therefore be introduced in physics as in biology.'[1]

We are still, perhaps, a long way from being able to identify life definitely in the mere details of what we commonly designate as inorganic phenomena; and one essential respect in which we cannot identify it is that we know nothing as yet corresponding in the apparent inorganic world to reproduction in living organisms, although in radio-active phenomena we seem to be in presence of what might be regarded as deaths of atoms. Our knowledge of how new atoms of any particular sort are formed is still in its infancy; but new discoveries may at any time throw such a light on this as will bridge what seems to be the greatest remaining gap between the organic and apparent inorganic.

Meanwhile we must, as it seems to me, hold to the conclusion that life, since it is a part of our perceived experience, though we can as yet see no clear way towards relating it in detail to existing physical ideas, must be regarded as ultimately inherent in what we at present picture as inorganic phenomena, and that it is only for practical reasons with present knowledge that we are compelled to separate organic from inorganic phenomena. We can thus adhere in the most thorough-going manner to the conception of evolution without making the unintelligible assumption involved in mechanistic biology.

[1] *Nature*, 18 April 1931.

In reality it is because of our faith in the ultimate consistency of our universe of experience that we must reject the idea that life has originated from mechanical conditions. This idea is inconsistent with what are found to be the characters of life, as referred to above. It cannot, therefore, be a true idea if, as philosophy assumes, consistency is the mark of truth. The rejection of the mechanistic conception of life carries with it the rejection of the theory that life has originated out of mechanical conditions.

In this connexion reference may be made to the conception of what has been called 'Emergent Evolution' by Professor Lloyd Morgan, and has been worked out in further philosophical detail by Professor Alexander in his book *Space, Time, and Deity*. According to this conception life originated as something new when a certain complexity of physical and chemical condition arose; and with a certain greater complexity, as it arises in the central nervous system of higher organisms, conscious experience originated.

It seems to me that this conception only hides away the gap which exists between mechanical and biological interpretation. No degree of physical and chemical complication brings us in any way nearer to the phenomena of life or conscious experience. The distinction between life and anything which can be expressed in terms of mechanical conceptions has already been discussed fully.

A similar criticism applies to the conception originated by Marx, and known as 'dialectical materialism'. It assumes a primitive self-existent physical world, out of which by a process of 'dialectic' similar to what Hegel postulated in the world of thought, higher states of existence develop. To 'dialectic' of this sort I can attach no more meaning than to 'emergent evolution', but dialectical materialism has recently come into much prominence as the official philosophy of the present Russian Government.

It is only on superficial examination that we seem compelled to conclude that all the remarkable characters of living organisms have been acquired through the chance action of a physical and chemical environment on more primitive organisms and ultimately on lifeless substances, these characters being transmitted to descendants, and through the influence of natural selection giving rise to different species.

Closer examination reveals a complete gap in this account. As already pointed out, the relation between organism and environment is no mere mechanical relation in which we can separate the influences of organism and environment—of 'nature' and 'nurture'. In the acquisition of a new character the organism is just as much active as the environment, and were it not so new characters would not be transmitted to descendants. It is only in the light of the distinctively biological conception of a life which embraces environment that evolution can be interpreted. Every new character is an active adaptation of pre-existing life, and its transmission to descendants is a sign that in the adaptation the life itself of the organism is expressing itself. Acquisition of a new character is always a distinctively biological phenomenon, just as life itself is. The controversy as to how far acquired characters can be inherited seems to me to turn largely on a misunderstanding of what the acquisition of a new character implies. If we attempt to attribute the acquisition to the mere influence of environment we can always also show that an hereditary factor is involved. In biological interpretation we can never separate organism from environment.

In the same way the attribution in individual development of all adult characters to the physical and chemical structure of its germinal material assumes that we can describe life as appertaining to physical and chemical structure apart from its environment. This we certainly cannot do. The chromosomes and chromomeres of a living germ-cell are an expression of its whole life, and its further life in essential connexion with embryonic and adult environment furnishes the only key to an understanding of their real nature. We can see their appearances under the microscope, but we must also see them with the mind's eye in the light of their relation to environment as revealed in their future development and past history.

Living organisms not only tend to maintain and reproduce themselves, but so far as is definitely known they also normally die after a certain period of life, although if they reproduce themselves their life is thus carried on indefinitely. We must, I think, regard this normal death as a feature characteristic of life. Normal death is sometimes regarded as a wearing out of the machinery of life; but this is evidently a quite unsuitable metaphor, since living structure, when we consider it closely, can easily be seen to be constantly renewing itself, so that it cannot be regarded as mere machinery which necessarily wears out. Normal death must apparently be regarded from the biological standpoint as a means by which room is made for further more definite development of life. When we consider the phenomena of life as a whole, including what the geological records reveal, we find life pushing itself forward into fresh forms which are on the whole more and more definitely characterized as regards either structure or life-history. Parasitic forms of life seem for instance to possess extraordinarily definite life-histories, though the visible forms of parasitic organisms may seem simplified or 'degenerate'.

We can thus consider life as continuously evolving, though from the standpoint of biology alone there is no meaning in discussing whether evolving forms of life are in any way better or more beautiful, since values have no meaning for biology. Normal death may be regarded as just an expression of the nature of life, and from this standpoint normal death becomes biologically intelligible when considered in conjunction with reproduction. Sexual reproduction can perhaps be regarded as a means of securing that a distinct, but only limited difference will exist between parent and offspring.

Death also follows commonly on accident or disease, and in this we can regard the supervention of death in individual organisms, or even in whole species, as from the biological standpoint an event which facilitates the further development of life by avoiding the very complex process of repair, healing, or adaptation, which would otherwise be required. Both death and reproduction are specifically biological phenomena, and we must interpret them from the standpoint of biology, not of physical science. We are so accustomed to the phenomenon of death that its specifically biological character does not ordinarily occur to us.

It is only generally, and not in detail, that we find ourselves compelled to apply biological interpretation. When we consider in minute detail various phenomena in the living body of an organism or in its environment we lose sight of what we otherwise interpret as life. A higher organism, for instance, seems to us to consist of individual molecules or atoms. The environment, also, seems to consist of separable physical parts and processes. Even when we correct the detailed view by a general one, it is only generally that we can apply the biological interpretation. Life thus appears as if it were a constant struggle against what is not life but only physical chaos.

It is, however, only in this apparent struggle that life can manifest itself as life. Life becomes meaningless if we regard it as other than an active struggle within otherwise unco-ordinated chaos; and the more clearly we realize how our universe appears apart from life, the more clearly does life appear to us. To take an instance, the more clearly we realize what is implied in the physically interpreted processes of diffusion, filtration, osmosis, and chemical affinity, the more clear does the co-ordination which is present in living metabolic activity become, and the more inadequate the attempts to interpret this activity, physically and chemically. Or, to take another instance, the more clearly we realize the physical interpretation of light, the more clearly can we appreciate the existence of physiological co-ordination in our experience of brightness and colour.

We may thus say that physical interpretation is involved in biological interpretation, and is indispensable in detail in spite of biological interpretation. But the fact that life appears to us as a struggle against chaos is in reality only part of the nature of life as essentially active; and we shall see that in higher planes of interpretation a similar character appears. Life is, however, not something apart from physical reality, but only the same reality seen and interpreted more fundamentally, and including within itself the chaotic elements which we cannot in detail interpret biologically.

When we look back, from the standpoint reached in the present chapter, at the categories or general conceptions which Kant, following Aristotle in the main, regarded as constitutive of the perceived world, it is evident that they now appear in a different light. Thus separation in space or time is no longer separation, but unity expressed in spatial or temporal relations. Cause and effect are no longer separable, since, as stimulus and response, they alike display manifestations of one life. Matter and energy, together with other conceptions, which from a Kantian standpoint would be separable, are similarly inseparable, and the other Kantian categories have changed correspondingly; while the conception of life, which was absent in the Kantian scheme, is now present as a principle which unites the Kantian categories in a sense not existing before. Thus the Kantian phenomenal world of perception has ceased to be a mechanical world, and now appears as a world of life, since life is involved in all perceived experience.

There is, however, an essential element in experience which biological interpretation does not cover, and this will be considered in the next chapter.

III

PHILOSOPHY AND PSYCHOLOGY

IN passing from what we interpret as mere life, such as not merely animals, including ourselves, but also plants and all lower organisms appear to exemplify, to conscious behaviour, we make a further great step towards realizing the nature of the experience which philosophy has to deal with. The whole of our experience is conscious experience, so that in dealing with conscious experience we are covering the whole of our experience.

Conscious experience reveals to us in perception what we cannot help regarding as a world independent of our individual perception of it. Our justification for doing so, and what is implied in this justification, will be discussed in the next chapter. But from the standpoint of individual psychology, as discussed in the present chapter, our perceived world is no more than what individual perception covers. If we imagine that we can make a jump from this to a self-existent physical world we have ignored the philosophical evidence, as given in Chapter I, which has shown that such a jump is not possible. We therefore cannot regard psychology as an analysis of the manner in which a self-existent physical world reveals itself to us, and we react to this world: we must take individual psychology as we find it, and endeavour to describe and analyse what it implies.

Conscious experience implies that in it we experience what is present as embodying, both spatially and temporally, various relationships in what is perceived. It does not embody merely direct awareness of what is perceived, but also a realization of the relationships. It thus embodies what we call ideas. These make both prediction and retrospect possible. Apart from ideas there would be no perceived world of inter-related objects, nor of any orderly world of experience such as the sciences describe.

But something more is implied in conscious experience. The objects and events perceived are not merely related to one another individually, but together constitute what we recognize as the interest of a percipient who is also an agent, in such a way that his perceptions constitute motives which with his corresponding conscious actions express effort at maintenance of the unity which we call his personality. Perception of what is of interest and conscious action are combined in the expression of personality, perception being no less an expression of personality than conscious action.

Let us now see how conscious behaviour is related, on the one hand, to what we interpret as the mere life of an organism, and on the other to what we interpret as no more than a physical world. In our interpretation of what we regard as mere life we do not assume the presence to the organism of a world of related objects, but only of stimuli present immediately. The behaviour of the mere organism is thus what can be called blind; but the stimuli and corresponding responses to them express tendency towards maintenance of the co-ordinated unity which we call the organism's life. For mere life there are no ideas, and therefore neither retrospect nor foresight, nor learning from experience; and it is by the presence or absence of retrospect and foresight that we distinguish conscious behaviour from mere life. Thus mere life implies much less than the personality of conscious experience. If we attribute conscious experience to an organism we are raising it to the level of personality.

In the case of what we interpret as no more than a physical world we are regarding our experience as that of a world of objects and events, with all the spatially and temporally ordered individual relationships which such a world implies. But we are disregarding completely the fact that the objects and events, together with the conscious acts which accompany them, are such as to represent in addition the co-ordinated and maintained unities of life and personality. The actual world of our conscious experience is much more than the world of physical science, though we may not realize this till we try to take life and conscious behaviour into account. In face of these, physical interpretation breaks down, and we also realize that even what we interpret as the inorganic world is more than this, as shown in the previous chapter. It is a world in which not only are our mere lives embodied, but which is of interest to percipient persons and enters into their personalities.

What for physical science appeared as only a physical body, and for biology as only a living organism, is for psychology a person, the centre of spatially and temporally ordered objects and events embodying active interest or personality. Our world is a world of personality, and we are only expressing this otherwise if we say that it is a spiritual world. If we called it an ideal world this would not express the fact that it embodies will, and not merely thought.

We can, and commonly do, regard the perceived world of objects and events apart, not only from what Kant pointed out as their essential relativity and the consequent abstract unity which a universe of relativity implies, but also apart from the fact of their much more concrete unity as constituting a world of personality. This is what, by a process of abstraction from reality, we do when we simply regard our universe as consisting of self-existent objects and events which our minds perceive. But for psychology as the scientific study of conscious behaviour no such abstraction from reality is possible.

We are making the same abstraction if we regard psychology as a science which studies the manner in which a real and independent physical world comes to appear to us as it does in conscious experience, and to react with our minds or souls. We are at present accustomed to assume as self-evident the existence of a purely physically interpreted world. But this assumption has not only been ruled out by the development of modern philosophy : it is also ruled out by the fact that the world of our conscious experience is a world, not merely of life, but of personality in the sense already explained. In the constitution of that world we as persons are intimately involved, and the conception of a world which, though it comes to be perceived, exists independently of perception of it, has no real meaning, however convenient it may be for certain purposes.

As will be shown later, personality is much more than mere individual personality, so that the world of our experience is no mere subjective experience, varying from person to person, but real in an objective sense. In the meantime, however, it is only what appears to us as individual personality that is under consideration.

For individual personality the conception of what is here and now, in distinction from what is elsewhere and past or future, acquires the meaning which it has for a perceived universe. If we could actually imagine a physical universe apart from its being perceived, but taking relativity into account, hereness and nowness would have no meaning for such a universe. Here would be anywhere, and now would be any time. It is, however, the *perceived and willed* universe centred in a person that we deal with in ordinary observation, so that what is here and now has an intelligible meaning.

In the case of mere life we can say that past behaviour of previous generations is represented in a present life. The specific life of an individual organism was regarded by Hering, in his book *Die Mneme*, as essentially due to memory, the organism remembering and repeating the ancestral behaviour of its race. In the individual life of a mere organism we cannot, however, distinguish what we can call memory; and if we did we should be attributing to it the ideas which characterize conscious behaviour. What we regard as a mere organism behaves, in both its development and its adult characters, as its parent organisms and their progenitors behaved; but this only exemplifies blind maintenance of the co-ordinated unity which we call a life. The special characters of this have gradually differentiated themselves in the course of evolution, this differentiation being necessarily recapitulated more or less in individual reproduction. To attribute this maintenance to the memory of past behaviour of the race is not necessary to our understanding of mere life, and only introduces obscurity. Memory is indeed a meaningless word apart from the ideas of a past in conscious relation to a present.

It is concrete active personality, and not the mere abstract and shadowy unity called 'mind', which is embodied in conscious experience. Reality now appears as concrete personality, and not as something which can be resolved into mere ideas. On this point it seems to me that we must break with any form of philosophy which can strictly speaking be called idealism, just as much as we are breaking with any form of physical realism, though not entirely with the spiritual realism, often called idealism, represented in the philosophy of Berkeley. Conscious experience is perceived experience, and perception, as Kant pointed out, implies unity extending over relations of both space and time. But unity in this sense, or in the similar sense implied in relativity physics, amounts to no more than an abstract scheme not affecting, except generally, the details of what is perceived, these details being no more than those of a universe as interpreted by the physical sciences. Kant's idealistic successors gave a much wider interpretation to the details, but the unity which they conceived as Absolute Mind, or the Absolute, was still a unity outside any detailed relation to what it covered, and might be likened to a God who did nothing but contemplate a very variegated universe of mere appearance. In this connexion I must refer to what seems to me the inadequacy of Bradley's conception of the Absolute, as represented in his book *Appearance and Reality*.

For personality the unity which it implies is active, like the unity in life, and is directly present in the details of perceived experience. It may be pointed out rightly that philosophy deals with much more than mere individual experience. This subject, however, will be discussed in the next chapter. At present we are only dealing with individual personality, which for common sense appears to us as something real and concrete, just as does the physical universe or the universe of life; and the universe of personality represents a unity which is actively present in its details, over time relations as well as space relations.

From the standpoint of personality either the physically interpreted universe, or the universe of life, is only abstractly interpreted, essential aspects of our actual experience having been left out of account. In so far as these aspects are taken into account in the universe of personalities we come much nearer to reality, just as we come nearer to reality in biological than in physical interpretation, though it is reality we are dealing with, however imperfectly, at each stage of interpretation. The inadequate treatment of biology by philosophical and other writers has, however, produced what appears as an almost insuperable division between physical interpretation and interpretation in terms of personality. For Descartes, for instance, physical reality was extended, and spiritual reality unextended. Ordinary common sense seems to leap easily over this gulf, but for deeper reflection the leap seems almost an impossible one, and to be only capable of being made with the help of hypotheses, such as divinely pre-established harmony, which either physical science or the psychological science which deals with personality must reject. There is no such gulf between physical and biological, or between biological and psychological interpretation. It is not very difficult to realize that biological interpretation is only physical interpretation transformed by taking into account our experience of actively maintained co-ordination in what we perceive. Nor is it difficult

to realize that psychological is only biological interpretation transformed by taking account of the fact
that our experience embodies conscious behaviour.

In psychology, regarded as the branch of theoretical
and applied knowledge which deals with individual
conscious behaviour, the conception of personality
is just as fundamental as the conception of life in biology. We can make a superficial distinction between
perceptions, motives, and conscious acts, but we
cannot separate them. What we perceive is perceived
in relation to our interest. It thus has the character
of a motive and is in essential relation to our conscious
actions. It is the same with our motives, which are
essentially bound up with perceptions and conscious
actions; and our conscious actions themselves would
be meaningless apart from this embodiment of perceptions as motives in the expression of personality.
The conception of value derives its meaning from
that of personality, since anything perceived can be
said to have value in proportion as personality is
expressed in it.

The representation of perceptions as mere impressions on a passive receiving mind is taken from traditional physical interpretation, which, as already seen,
cannot possibly express adequately the facts of mere
life, let alone those of conscious experience.

In the history of philosophy, psychology fell between the two stools of mechanistic realism and an
abstract spiritualism represented in the conception of
a soul independent of its body. Psychology had thus

no sound theoretical basis, and has commonly been represented as based on a dualistic conception of mind and body, with all the weakness of the dualism of Descartes. Kant, in particular, regarded psychology as an impossible science. Others have endeavoured to give it a pseudo-scientific appearance by splitting its treatment up into that of various separate psychical faculties, which, as just pointed out, are not separable. In recent times it has often become a field for either attempted mechanistic psychology or for empirical treatment in which a clear conception of personality is practically absent, but which is a convenient dumping place for phenomena, such as those of contrast as embodied in Fechner's law, of which neither mechanistic nor vitalistic physiology could give any interpretation. The conception of personality extending over both temporal and spatial environment is required if we are to bring order and intelligibility into psychology. Without this conception the facts become altogether distorted. A soul distinct from body is as unreal as a body distinct from soul.

At this point, however, reference must be made to a comparatively recent and certainly very valuable development in psychology. This is what is known by its German name of 'Gestalt' psychology, as given to it by its chief founder, Professor Köhler. He pointed out the barrenness of the attempts which have been made to found psychology on either mechanistic physiology (by the 'behaviourist' school) or on nothing but introspection (by the 'introspectionist' school), these two schools representing, as it were, the two horns of the dilemma which results from Cartesian dualism. He then proceeded to show that what appears to us in perception is not made up out of isolated sense-data but consists primarily of integrated objects—the 'forms' of Gestalt psychology. In this way psychology escapes from the incoherencies to which the Cartesian dilemma leads.

As already pointed out above, it is with a world of objects of perception, and neither of imaginary isolated sense-data nor equally imaginary self-existent objects and events in the physical sense, that psychology deals. This fundamental fact is embodied in Gestalt psychology. It is clear to me, however, that psychology must go much further than this. The objects which we perceive are not isolable or indifferent to one another, but together constitute the actively maintained unity which we call personality. The reasons for this conclusion have already been stated.

For physical interpretation of our experience perceptions are merely events in our own brains, entirely different from events outside though indirectly connected with them. Such interpretation does express the facts in a rudimentary way, but quite inadequately. Locke and Berkeley followed out the consequences of this inadequate expression, and the natural result was that Hume abolished even the receiving mind or brain, leaving, as he imagined, only the impressions.

A perceived object is no mere isolated phenomenon, but only exists in so far as it is an expression of actively maintained personality, and in a world which must be regarded as a world of personality, though we can also, by abstracting from essential aspects of this world, regard it artificially as a mere physical world, or as no more than a biological world in which perception and volition are regarded in the same manner as physiological stimulus and response.

From the standpoints of pure mathematical, physical, or biological science our perceptions are not regarded as an expression of personality. We are artificially regarding our experience in a detached manner, and disregarding the fact of its being perceived and of its embodying our interest, although we actually make use of our scientific interpretation in furthering the interests of ourselves and others. All that we thus interpret belongs in fact to our world of personality, but it is treated as if it were without personal interest to us, and in these sciences we are regarding our experience in this artificial manner. In reality we are only taking into account certain aspects of our actual experience, the fundamental fact that all this experience is of specifically personal interest or value being disregarded. Thus the scientific treatment involves abstraction, and this is carried to an extreme extent in mere mathematical treatment of our experience.

The advantage of this abstract treatment is that where knowledge of our own interest or that of others

P

is defective in detail we can nevertheless interpret details in such a manner as is often sufficient for the occasion. If, for instance, we measure the volume and mass of a perceived object or determine its chemical constitution, the knowledge thus represented may be sufficient for certain practical purposes, though this meagre knowledge tells us nothing directly about the biological significance of what is perceived, or its value—the place which it occupies in the maintenance of our interest. However much physical or chemical knowledge we may accumulate about the object, this knowledge remains by itself essentially partial and abstract. It must do so because of the abstract nature of such scientific interpretation. But when we can bring this partial knowledge into relation with the rest of our experience of personality, it ceases to be abstract.

In our rudimentary conscious experience we do not regard objects abstractly, but as of interest to us. Abstract scientific interpretation is an extremely useful artifice which men have devised for certain limited practical purposes. It is a mistaking of this artificial representation for a complete representation of experience that has given rise to such forms of belief as materialism or the Pythagorean attempt to regard quantitative relations as the essence of reality. Purely physical or mathematical reality is a mere image of our own creating with practical objects in view.

The rigid conclusions which Kant reached in his *Critique of Pure Reason* with regard to perceived experience rendered it impossible for him to treat, not only biological, but also psychological phenomena as distinctively present in our perceived experience. Both biological and psychological phenomena thus appeared to him incapable of being perceived except in the light of physical conceptions; and he points this out clearly, thus excluding the possibility of any such treatment of biology or psychology as had been attempted by previous philosophical or scientific writers. In reality both the specific biological and specific psychological interpretation of our perceived experience are just as real as the specific physical interpretation, and the psychological interpretation is merely the biological interpretation transformed or carried further because actual experience of conscious behaviour compels us to do so. We perceive, not mere physical or biological phenomena, but a world of our own interests and personalities and those of others; and when we see persons it is persons with their interests that we see, and not mere physical objects or living organisms. For Descartes, with his mistaken separation of mind from matter, the persons and living organisms we see were necessarily no more than physical objects, and this idea still persists in much of present-day science and literature, along with the idea that psychology can only be pursued by introspection, so that comparative psychology is impossible.

The inference that psychology can only be pursued by introspection results from the survival in popular thought of the Cartesian dualism discussed in Chapter I. But the idea that it cannot be pursued at all as a science is the product of Kant's narrow conception of what is revealed in perception. A world of psychological experience is just as clearly perceived as what we interpret as a physical world, so that there is no hindrance to what we can regard as its objective study in the conscious behaviour of men and animals.

The transition from biological to psychological interpretation involves a very far-reaching extension in the interpretation of our experience. It not only implies that we do not experience any event or object apart from what surrounds them both spatially and temporally, but that we do not do so apart from the manifestation in them of actively maintained and co-ordinated unity extending over time as well as space. How we interpret them, and how we behave towards them depends on this. A person and what he perceives, remembers, anticipates, wills, and consciously does are manifestations of this unity in so far as they are anything definable. We perhaps seem to experience mere physical events which are outside this unity, but, as Kant showed, mere isolated happenings have no meaning in our experience, and the foregoing reasoning shows in addition that in whatever enters into our experience personality is manifested.

As already mentioned, this does not imply the incredible conception that the universe of our experience is only a subjective universe of individual personalities. That it is much more than this will be shown in the next chapter.

Let us endeavour to regard conscious behaviour, including memory and foresight, from nothing but the standpoint of traditional physical interpretation. This, practically speaking, is what Descartes endeavoured to do in his *Passions of the Soul*. From this standpoint the peculiarities in the reactions of a conscious organism are due to the peculiarities of its structure, and particularly the structure of its highly developed sense-organs and brain. Memory is due to traces left in the brain structure by previous reactions, and foresight is a tendency of new reactions to follow in the tracks of previous similar reactions. Consciousness itself is just an accompaniment of changes occurring in the brain substance, though how these changes give rise to consciousness is completely mysterious. Consciousness is thus something localized in the brain, and, so far as we know, a unique accompaniment of the extremely complex physical and chemical processes which occur in a central nervous system.

This general conception accords with many facts. For instance, there is the fact that any severe injury to the brain, or interference with its blood-supply, entails loss of consciousness, while injurious substances which reach it, or a deficiency or excess in substances which are normally present, cause mental disturbances or even more serious effects. A localized injury to the brain may, moreover, cause loss of some particular capacity or particular form of memory. The more we learn as to the physiology of the brain, the more facts do we discover which seem to be consistent with the general conception which has just been referred to; and as a matter of fact we cannot help making practical use of this conception. It appears, or may appear, to be only common sense, and is indeed inevitable if we start from the common-sense assumption that traditional physical interpretation represents reality. As already pointed out, traditional physical interpretation is of the utmost practical service.

But now let us look at the facts more closely. From the standpoint of physical science each conscious reaction depends essentially on a host of conditions, more and more of which are being gradually revealed by physiological and psychological research. In the first place it depends on a multitude of what appear to be extremely definite physical and chemical conditions, summed up as a 'normal' structure and internal environment. From a physical and chemical standpoint the development and maintenance of this normal structure and environment are wholly unintelligible, as was pointed out in the previous chapter.

In the second place it depends on other nervous influences conveyed from and to all parts of the body and its environment, and particularly from various parts of the brain itself, including parts in which the traces conditioning memory are stored. Hence we cannot localize a conscious nervous reaction in any one place. All sorts of other reactions in different parts of the brain and its external environment are inseparably fused with any conscious reaction which we endeavour to follow. But this fusion occurs in a manner which embodies the maintenance and continuity of personal interest, including relations to both past and anticipated events. Ordinary physical conceptions lead us to a mere unco-ordinated fusion of innumerable events, but to no conception whatever as to how these events form the definite active pattern which we are familiar with as that of ourselves in a co-ordinated environment, both spatial and temporal, of what is of interest to us.

To regard memory as a mere expression of physical traces left in the brain does not tell us why memories flash out just as our interest calls for them. Memory is like an immense encyclopedia with the magic property of always opening at the required place and telling us the spatial, temporal, and other relationships of what participates in our interest, including future events. We cannot separate memory from anticipation. All our experience possesses a similar character. What is relevant to our interest starts out into prominence as our interest requires, and in this respect foresight resembles memory. Not only our brains and bodies but all the elements in what we perceive, or will, embody our personality, and mere physical interpretation of them is wholly inadequate and thus fails grossly.

When, finally, we consider what can be meant by

consciousness as an event, or series of events, occurring in the brain substance, we are confronted by all
the difficulties which were discussed in Chapter I,
and led up to Kant's conclusion that in the world
which we know as a perceived world, each distinguishable element is constituted by its relations to
other elements, so that to speak of perception as
something occurring in some particular part of it
and at some particular time, is without meaning. To
the world of perception there are no external limits
in either space or time, since space and time themselves are only relations within the world of perception. It may appear to us at first as if in perceiving
anything we are only perceiving it here and now, but
in actual fact we are also perceiving what is around
it in both space and time.

It is not that physical description of conscious
behaviour is not satisfactory up to a certain point,
but that it is totally inadequate to furnish any intelligible description of conscious behaviour as a whole.
We cannot describe separate events or other elements
in our conscious experience, but we can describe the
events in their essential relationship to one another
as together forming an actively maintained unity of
personality, extending over both temporal and spatial
relations. The elements in this unity involve one
another, so that the unity is expressed in each element. The elements, moreover, embody interest and
values which are actively maintained; and it is no
mere intellectual perception that they embody. They

embody what involves will, and is called, in a single word, personality.

Physical analysis is thus a relatively impotent means with which to attempt a description of the facts presented by conscious behaviour. We cannot dispense with the conception of active personality which is present in all the phenomena studied, including their relations both spatially and temporally. Those who set out to dispense with the conception of personality have set out on an inherently impossible task. What we discover is personality and nothing less. In our bodily structures, no less than in our environments, we are aware of personality, and any mere physical interpretation of them is quite inadequate. The 'me' of common sense is not just a physical body, but the 'me' which embodies personality, with all its multitudinous relations in spatial and temporal arrangement.

When, however, we examine the unity which exists in personality it appears at once that it is only in a general sense that this unity exists. In endless matters of detail we can only trace it imperfectly. Although the relations of persons to their environments, including their own bodies, embody on the whole the unity of personality, yet in a great mass of conscious experience we cannot trace this unity in detail. Things happen regardless of our capacity for understanding or dealing with them satisfactorily, so that our environment appears as to this extent something outside our personality. The best we can do with regard to these details as such is to interpret them as far as possible in terms of abstract science. But they belong nevertheless to our conscious experience as a whole, and when we take this into account it is evident that they are not outside personality, but inside it as something imperfectly defined.

The fact that endless matters of detail in our experience cannot be interpreted directly as the expression of personality reminds us of the similar fact with regard to life, and is of equally fundamental significance. When we consider personality we find that it would have no meaning except in relation to what is otherwise more or less chaotic. Personality is essentially active. All its manifestations are active, and this would not be the case apart from elements on which its activity is exercised. Yet from a wider philosophical standpoint these elements are within itself, so that personality appears as continuously developing out of what is imperfect or indefinite within itself. This is the real significance of there always being a now for personality.

In so far as personality appears as incompletely expressed in our experience we can only interpret this experience physically or biologically. Hence personality appears as a continuous overcoming of physical and biological elements in our experience. If we regard these elements as outside personality they appear as something entering into it from outside. Thus 'the unconscious', as a blind manifestation of physical or biological phenomena, may be interpreted as constantly entering into personality. Since, however, the elements in question form part of our experience, they are not outside personality, but an incomplete manifestation of it. In all of what we may interpret as mere blind biological instinct entering into conscious experience, personality with its accompanying responsibility and control is also present. Personality is never a mere playground of blind instincts. In so far as we are conscious of what might otherwise be regarded as blind instincts they enter into personality, and in them personality becomes, or is capable of becoming, more and more fully manifested.

An organism which is conscious appears for us no longer a mere organism, but a person. In the higher animals we seem to perceive personality almost as clearly as in human beings. Just, moreover, as life is physico-chemical activity perceived or interpreted more fully, or in its fuller manifestation, so personality is life perceived in its fuller manifestation. A person, moreover, is an actual or clearly perceived person, and no mere piece of machinery, or living organism guided by a soul, or to which consciousness has been added as a mere epiphenomenon. Nor do we express the facts if we say that consciousness is something everywhere present in mere material processes as such, though it only becomes aware of itself in what, from the standpoint of physical science, is the extremely complex process of life in higher organisms. In the perception of conscious behaviour as such we are no longer perceiving what can be interpreted partially as mere physico-chemical or biological activity. If we endeavour to read personality into details which we otherwise interpret as simply physico-chemical or biological activity, we can only do so by an act of vain unmeaning imagination. Conscious experience or personality is emphatically not something merely added to details which we otherwise interpret physically or biologically.

In psychology, which is the department of knowledge and practice which deals with personality, we penetrate more deeply into the nature of our perceived world than when we regard it more partially, as in physical or biological interpretation.

When we look back on the attempt to interpret the facts of personality physically, and the partial success of this attempt, we can see that this partial success depends on the assumption that the physical interpretation of our experience corresponds to reality. Once we have made this common-sense assumption we are carried forward by it into our experience of personality till we finally land in incoherency; and there seems to be no definite point at which we can stop.

It is the initial assumption that is incorrect. The physical interpretation of our experience is only a partial one, as has already been pointed out, and its partial nature becomes evident when we attempt to apply it to life, and still more evident when we attempt to apply it to the facts of conscious experience. When we speak of physical or chemical events conditioning or determining conscious behaviour we are endeavouring to apply a mode of interpretation which cannot apply, since the actual relationship between person and environment cannot be described in terms of physical interpretation, but only in terms of personality which extends over environment in both spatial and temporal relations. The partial success which we seem to meet with through applying physical interpretation to conscious behaviour is thus only present when we take no account of what is characteristic in the facts of conscious experience.

Let us consider further what is implied in personality. Just as we not merely perceive living organisms, but at the same time the physiological environments from which they cannot in perception or thought be separated, so we cannot separate persons from their personal environments or belongings. These personal environments belong to their personalities; and just because conscious behaviour is behaviour in which interpretation of the past is carried over into the present and future interpretation and behaviour, personal environment extends back into the past, and projects itself into the future, besides extending indefinitely in the spatial present. As will appear more fully in the next chapter, neither time nor space supplies limits for personality, and temporal and spatial arrangement is arrangement within personality, and not in anything outside it. Our whole universe is a universe of perceived phenomena in which all that is perceived embodies what is part of ourselves.

Just as a living organism is regarded as an *active*

manifestation of life, and the same active manifestation is present in the biological environment which cannot in thought be separated from it, so a person and all his perceived world, thoughts, motives, and acts, are *active* manifestations of personality. As Schopenhauer in particular pointed out in his book *Die Welt als Wille und Vorstellung*, we cannot separate thought from will; and as it seems to me, one of the great defects of much other post-Kantian German philosophy, and particularly the Hegelian philosophy, was just this artificial separation of thought from will, or subordination of will to thought. All our perceptions have a motive aspect as entering into our willed behaviour. What we will is also perceived or imagined, and what we perceive embodies the interest expressed in our behaviour. Thus we cannot separate perception and will, any more than we can in biological interpretation separate stimulus from response, or, apparently, in ultimate physical interpretation separate substance from its activity, as was pointed out on page 24. On superficial interpretation perception, volition, memory, and anticipation appear as different faculties, but when we examine them more closely it appears that none of them has any real meaning apart from the others.

The fact that personality is essentially active implies that it is a manifestation of itself in what is otherwise a world in which it is not yet realized—a world which is relatively speaking one of chaos. Yet if this world were outside personality it would mean nothing in what is essentially a world of experience. It is within the world of personality, and nevertheless personality is only in the most general and imperfect sense revealed in it, so that personality represents a constant active struggle to realize itself. This is why for personality there is always a 'now', representing what is new and which illuminates the nature of both the future and the past.

If we fail to recognize that the unity represented in personality embodies also a constant struggle we have mistaken the nature of personality. It is something which only realizes itself in struggle. The chaos which appears to us within it is an essential element in its very being. In this respect personality resembles life, though on a higher plane. By interpreting biologically, or even physically, the details in our experience where we cannot trace the coordination of personality, we can at least throw light on them, and we are constantly doing this.

What we call humanistic study cannot be regarded as less than psychology applied in various directions. To treat, for instance, history, which is sometimes done, as a mixture of astronomy, geology, and biology with psychological interpretation can only lead to the same confusion as is inherent in all attempts to treat personality as a mere addition to matter or life. History deals essentially with the manifestations of personality, and if as we pass backwards in time we lose sight of the manifestations of personality we also lose sight of history.

We find that in all ordinary occupations we are dealing with personality and its interests, so that, if we regard psychology as a department of knowledge, we are applying it constantly. Even when we are also applying physical, chemical, or biological knowledge in practical pursuits, success always involves the application of psychology, since we are at the same time dealing with persons and human affairs. This aspect of an occupation is the most fundamental, because when we regard it philosophically it takes us nearer to reality than does more abstract scientific knowledge. It is for this reason that what is usually called the humanistic side of education is so important, and takes precedence over other aspects. Education in the capacity for understanding persons and their interests, and in making oneself understood by others, is all-important.

The attempt is sometimes made to base psychology as a science on physiology or even physical science, and to make use of it in education on this basis. This appears to me an index of the rudimentary ideas which, in spite of its great importance, are still current as to the nature and fundamental conceptions of psychology. I can myself see no other firm basis for psychology than the conception of personality, as already discussed in this chapter, together with the reasons which give to this conception its fundamental importance.

The conception of what is of value is implied in the conception of personality, and represents any detail of what is actively maintained in our persons and personal environments. What is 'pleasing' is what tends to be consciously maintained, and in virtue of this it is of value. In one way or another it represents what we will to maintain or develop; and what is displeasing to ourselves is what we correspondingly avoid or alter. Pleasure is nothing which stands by itself, apart from the realization in it of personality. From the standpoint of individual psychology what is of value to one personality is different from what is of value to another. Needs and tastes differ, and in the case of personal belongings which are transferable this leads to transfer for mutual advantage, and to the expression of values in terms of some standard, or as a market value in money.

When we look at our surroundings from this standpoint they become an economic world. A state becomes an economic organization, and the conflicts between states become economic conflicts. That this is, however, a very imperfect standpoint will appear in the next chapter.

We must, I think, distinguish what is simply pleasing to us from the standpoint of individual personality from what is right or beautiful. There is far more in rightness or beauty than what is merely pleasing to individuals, or what can be assessed in terms of other values; but this subject will be discussed in the last chapter.

Just as in living organisms we can distinguish subordinate units of life, each contributing its share to a common life, so, in the sphere of psychology, are individual personalities subordinated more or less to wider individual personalities, represented, for instance, by families, tribes, or states. In the group personalities thus represented there need be nothing essentially different from what we regard as individual personalities; and what we ordinarily regard as realization of individual interest is usually in agreement at the same time with realization of the wider interest, though where this is not so the wider interest may take precedence. It is perfectly natural for both men and animals to sacrifice their individual interests for others with whom their interests are in any way bound up naturally. Here again, however, what appears as right is much more than what we can interpret as the mere interest of a group personality.

The difference between biological and psychological interpretation or perception is similar to the difference between physical and biological interpretation. There is no gross clashing between psychological and biological interpretation, just as there is none between biological and physical interpretation. Psychological interpretation is only biological interpretation carried forward into psychological interpretation because the experience concerned necessitates this carrying forward, just as the experience concerned necessitates the carrying forward of physical into biological interpretation. It is always the same universe that we are interpreting, though we are interpreting it more fundamentally in biology than in physical science, and more fundamentally in psychology than in biological science. We must also realize that the psychological interpretation extends over the whole of our experience. This is implied in the fact that our universe is a universe of conscious experience.

Nevertheless, psychological interpretation is always imperfect in detail, and we fill up the imperfections by means of physical and biological interpretation. We cannot do more than this, but over all the details general psychological interpretation extends, leaving nothing outside it.

The gulf which Kant created in his philosophy between the subject-matters of his three Critiques arose from the rigid character of the conceptions or categories which he regarded as determining our perceptions. He was still under the predominating influence of physical conceptions, or of the Aristotelian logic which was embodied in them. There is no rigid boundary which prevents our interpreting biologically or psychologically what we may previously have only interpreted physically. Hence the experience discussed in the two later Critiques is not something apart from the world of ordinary perception, but the same world interpreted more deeply, or perceived more fully. Kant was therefore mistaken in drawing a fixed line between the world of perception and what he discussed in the two later Critiques.

We can now follow life in some detail from generation to generation, but we cannot follow personality in the same manner. Nor can we follow either life or personality in endless details of what we are therefore led to call the inorganic world. When, however, we regard our experience philosophically as a whole, the deeper psychological interpretation extends over all of it, though not, as will appear in the succeeding chapter, in the form of mere individual personality. The world of our experience is a world of conscious experience, and therefore a psychological world of interest and values. On this point there is no room for compromise between philosophy and any of the sciences. Those for whom traditional physical interpretation appears to represent ultimate reality are simply accepting impossible and out-of-date philosophy. It is only when we disregard essential elements in what we perceive that the conception of physical reality appears to correspond finally with our experience.

The fact that we cannot follow personality in detail from generation to generation, and that we gradually lose sight of it as we go back in history, is often taken as evidence that personality cannot be regarded as anything more than the outcome of what we interpret as physical or biological conditions which we can trace backwards much further. Just, however, as we can only trace the nature of an embryo in the adult organism which it develops into, so we can only trace the real nature of what appears to us as mere physical or biological reality by what it develops into. We can attach no meaning to the idea of

conscious experience, or even life, being a modification
of mere physically interpreted reality. We are therefore compelled to assume that what, as we pass backwards in time, appears to us as becoming no more
than physical reality is actually much more than this,
and that the germs of personality are present in it.
Apart from this consideration there remains the fact
that the world of physical science, looked at as a
whole, is a world of perception, and thus not outside
personality. Time itself, as Kant showed, is not outside what he called mind, and the foregoing discussion
has shown that what Kant called mind is in reality
personality, though the fuller discussion of this point
must be postponed to the next chapter.

The fact of death, no less than the fact of birth and
of evolution from what appear to us as inorganic conditions, appears also as a rounding off of personality
by inorganic conditions, or at least as an end or beginning of personality. In the succeeding chapter we shall
see, however, that personality is not mere individual
personality. Just as from a biological standpoint
the fact of individual death can be interpreted as no
termination of life itself, so from the standpoint of
personality the death of an individual is no termination of personality, but only of a particular form in
which wider personality has temporarily manifested
itself.

The account which was given of biology in the
previous chapter implies that there is at present widespread confusion with regard to the real aims and

scope of biology as a science. But this is even more true of psychology as at present very commonly represented; and the source of the confusion in psychology is of a similar nature to that in biology. On the one hand the 'mind' or 'soul', like the 'vital principle', is regarded as something independent of a physically interpreted body and environment; and on the other, psychological phenomena, like biological phenomena, are regarded as being essentially physico-chemical processes, though mysteriously accompanied by consciousness in the higher centres of the brain.

The reasons why the latter, or materialistic, hypothesis must be rejected have already been stated very fully above; and the preceding discussion in the present chapter implies the rejection of the former hypothesis. It may, however, be desirable at this point to discuss the former hypothesis further. Current discussion turns round the question whether or not the 'will' is free. If our actions were determined by influences from a physical environment our wills would not be free; and the assumption that conscious action is not so determined is an essential part of the former hypothesis.

This matter appears, however, quite differently in the light of the preceding discussion. Our psychological environment, whether looked at spatially or temporally, is not something outside our personality, but included in it. The perceptions or motives which are represented as possessing an influence on our will are thus not influences from outside our personality, but influences arising within it. In their influences upon us our own personalities are being expressed. In what a man perceives or remembers or anticipates, and in what motives appeal effectively to him, his whole personality or character is expressed. The idea of perceptions or motives influencing him from without is taken from mere physical interpretation. Only if he is character-less or backboneless does he become what might perhaps be described as a playground for chaotic motives. In this case we may either call him a bad man or not a man at all; and we can hardly describe him as free. But a man is free in proportion as his perceptions and actions express his personality, in spite of the endless variety of fresh forms which per-ceptions and motives take. The forms in which his perceptions, memories, anticipations, and motives appear to him express the unity of his personality, just as, on a plane of lower interpretation, the influences of its environment on an organism express the unity of its life.

There is also another sense in which personality must be regarded as free or possessing spontaneity. The 'now' of personality implies that what is new is constantly appearing in personality, and cannot be predicted because it alters what appears to us as the past as well as the future. The 'now' which is always present to personality implies the presence of what cannot be predicted.

If, further, as a contribution to psychology, we proceed to distinguish essentially separable 'faculties' of mind, such as perception, volition, memory, or the power of experiencing pleasure, we only produce confusion. We cannot separate perception from the active motive influence which is part of it and passes into overt action; and in all perception memory and anticipation are involved. Apart from memory the perception of even such apparently simple things as definite extension, motion, or mass would be impossible; and the personal interests embodied in all our perceptions would not exist. Pleasure, also, is nothing in itself, and only realization of personality.

In the present epoch of European civilization we have become accustomed to the assumption that the traditional physical interpretation of our visible and tangible experience corresponds to reality itself. As a consequence, it seems natural to us to discuss the relation of mind to body, and to regard mind as conditioned by a physical body and its physical environment—for instance to look upon mind as dependent on the physical development of the body, and particularly of the brain and its structural development. What we call psychological phenomena are quite clearly correlated with what we call bodily structure. But, as already pointed out, we have no right at all to regard physical structure and physical environment as existing outside personality, or the physical interpretation of our bodies or environment as anything more than a partial and imperfect interpretation which is superseded when we interpret our bodies and environment as expressing personality. In the common-sense interpretation of our experience we also pass lightly from a common-sense physical interpretation to an equally common-sense, though inconsistent, interpretation in terms of personality and all that pertains to personality. For the latter interpretation what we perceive as persons are actual persons, and no mere physical bodies containing minds or souls. The environments of persons are also no mere physical environments, but embodiments of the interests and values involved in personality. It is also true that for common sense the humanistic branches of knowledge and activity represent reality even more fundamentally than does physical or biological science.

In flitting from a physical to a psychological interpretation, as if both interpretations could be fundamental, common sense does not realize the contradictions then involved in these interpretations. But the contradictions exist, and the manner in which philosophy deals with them has already been pointed out. For various practical purposes it is useful to regard the body as a physical structure, and its environment as a physical environment. Philosophy points out, however, that this physical interpretation is only a superficial interpretation, which must not be allowed to confuse us through being regarded as more than a superficial interpretation. This does not, however, prevent us from accepting and justifying it as a superficial interpretation of great practical use.

In the present chapter personality has been considered as if it were only individual personality among other personalities. The facts which take us beyond this limited view of personality will be discussed in the next chapter. Meanwhile we can see that in the interpretation of our experience we have been carried much beyond the point which Kant had reached, and much beyond the point which we reached in Chapter II. Our individual experience now appears as representing, however imperfectly, the concrete active manifestation of personality, each element in which has its existence in relation to the other elements both in time and in space. Neither mere physical interpretation nor mere biological interpretation expresses this aspect of our experience, and the conception of personality takes the place of the shadowy entity called mind.

IV

PHILOSOPHY AND RELIGION

IT is not the object of this chapter to discuss rudimentary forms of religion, or the special forms
which it has taken elsewhere than in Western civilizations, but only religion as we find it in the latter or
closely related civilizations.

By religion is commonly understood a system of
conduct and of belief, an integral part of which refers
to what are regarded as historical events, these, however, being different in different forms of religion.
Thus we come to speak of religions as if they were
essentially different from one another: also as if
religion were something added from without to
ordinary experience. In the present chapter I shall
endeavour to treat religion as what it appears to me
to be, namely, something permeating the whole of
experience, whether on the side of perception or
conscious behaviour. This involves, as we shall see,
treating under the heading of religion what is usually
treated separately as ethics, theory of knowledge, and
aesthetics.

Religions seem to afford sanctions for whatever
may be regarded as right or good in action, ultimately
true, or to be treated as of fundamental or sacred value
as beautiful, or an expression of goodness, or truth.
Even, however, when overt forms of religious belief
are absent, ideas of what is right, true, and beautiful

remain, however much these ideas may differ in detail among different persons. We shall now inquire what is implied in the existence of such ideas, and how they are related generally to our experience.

In the previous chapter personality was discussed as if it only signified one personality among other personalities, with one interest among other interests. But our actual experience is of other individual personalities besides our own, and consequently of other individual interests besides our own. We find, nevertheless, that our interests identify themselves with theirs, and their interests with ours, so that we have what we call mutual duties, and that these duties take precedence over mere individual interests, or are what we call sacred. This does not mean simply that there is a subordination of individual interests to group interests, as in the case of what has been referred to as group personality, but that individual interests enter into what otherwise appear as different individual interests. The distinction is a fundamental one, and failure to make it leads often to confused political and other ideas.

The perception of mutual duty, since it is independent of mere individual interest or personality, must be regarded as representing what is objective or independent of mere individual perception.

Honesty, charity, and tolerance are duties which, in so far as they do not clash with one another, take precedence over self-interest or the interest of group personalities. This applies just as much to the mutual relations between families or nations as to the relations between individuals. Our recognition of mutual duty carries us beyond the world of mere individual personality. We do not derive the fact of duty from either self-interest or the interest of a group personality such as a state, though duty commonly appears to us first as that to other members of a family or state.

There is a further fundamental respect in which our interest is not merely individual. We are interested in what we regard as truth, by which we mean what is objectively true, or what holds good apart from all merely individual interests or personalities; and the search for it appears also to us as sacred, and its furtherance a sacred duty. The truth we can reach in any particular case may be only limited or relative, as in the different sciences, but is none the less sacred on this account as a contribution to fuller truth. We regard the world of our experience as being, in spite of the defects in our interpretation of it, an objective world which it is our duty to understand or perceive rightly, and thus be able to act rightly. The conviction that our experience is of a real world, and not a mere individual subjective appearance, is present throughout all our experience, and we are constantly verifying this conviction. Philosophy itself is nothing but search after the truth which we regard as being present throughout all our experience, and as ultimately consistent with the partial aspects of truth which we find in the sciences. But the search for truth is not something which we can ascribe to mere individual interest or personality, and the fact that we do search for it is clear evidence that what may appear to us as only individual personality is much more than this.

The realization that our perceived world is something independent of our mere individual perception of it is commonly taken as evidence that the world as interpreted physically is something independent of perception of it. But, as shown in Chapter I, this conception is not consistent with our experience. Our experience is, as shown in Chapter III, that of personality, so that the only manner in which we can interpret the element of objective truth in it is as a manifestation of personality which embraces all individual personalities. It is never a mere physical or biological world which we perceive, but a world not only perceived by us, but in which we are responsibly involved, so that at every point it refers us to duties; and it is as such that we treat it in the applied sciences, for instance in engineering or medical work. As no more than a physically interpreted world it is only an abstraction from experience. As the manifestation of all-embracing personality or God, it is a world of truth, duty, and beauty, in which we are in some sort participating.

We find also that in still another respect our interest is not merely individual. In what we perceive, apart from our own individual interests and those of other individuals, we are aware of interest in the inherently co-ordinated unity which we experience around us, and designate as beautiful. Interest in this enters also into what may at first have appeared as mere individual interest, and, like our interest in duty to one another, takes precedence over mere individual interest, so that beauty has also a sacred character, and the furthering of it is likewise a sacred duty. In experiencing what is beautiful we recognize an inherent wholeness or co-ordination, apart altogether from either our own individual interests or those of others. The ordered beauty of the stars, to take one instance, is an overpowering experience, appealing to all men, and the more so the more they study the heavens. It was Plato who first recognized that in our ideas of goodness, truth, and beauty we are in touch with deeper reality.

Hence apparent individual personality implies much more than mere individual personality. Without losing their individual characters, personalities, including all their concrete environments, are united in such a way that each person has his special duties to perform as regards right, truth, and beauty; and binding authority is present among these duties. This binding character has nothing external or artificial in it; it belongs to our own personalities. But as it is not attributable to mere individual personality, but covers the whole of experience, we cannot interpret it as less than the manifestation in us of all-embracing personality, and this, as it seems to me, is what is meant by God. Thus we must regard what

appears to us to be true, good, or beautiful as a manifestation in us, however imperfect, of divine perception, will, and activity. In so far as we are endeavouring to further what appears to us as true, good, and
beautiful, God is present in us, and knowledge of
God is communicated to us.

It seems clear that mere individual personality
cannot account for our strivings after truth, right, and
beauty; but are we not making a leap in the dark when
we interpret them as manifestations in us of what men
call God? There would certainly be such a leap if we
regarded God as an individual person among other
persons and things. But there is no leap in the dark if
we regard God as present to and in us. If we did not
make use of the word God we should require to use
another word with the same import. We must also
attribute personality to God because the seekings
after truth, right, and beauty have no meaning outside the unity of personality as perceived and willed
unity. Their authority can be nothing less than that
of supreme personality.

We thus realize the existence of all-embracing
personality or God, present to and in individual personality, and in perceptions which can be regarded as
representing, however imperfectly, what is not merely
valid or true for one personality among others, but
for all personalities. We also reach a conception of
what appears objectively right in action, and of values
which are not merely pleasing to individuals, but appear objectively beautiful. As was shown in Chapter I,

a consideration of the merely physically interpreted universe gives us a conception of God as all-embracing unity. But it is only in our ethical, intellectual, and aesthetic experience that we realize the existence of God as all-embracing personality, present in ourselves. Apart from the presence of God in us our experience of what could be regarded as an objective world would be unintelligible. Our world would only appear as a fleeting subjective world. And apart from our experience of goodness, beauty, and truth God would no longer appear to us as personal and the source of all that is good, true, and beautiful.

As it appears to me, religion, whether it is overtly recognized as religion or not, enters into our experience in so far as we endeavour to realize in perception and behaviour the objective aspects of our experience. A mere collection of theological beliefs not based on personal experience of truth, right, and beauty may have considerable historical or humanistic interest, but is not by itself religion, and may also be associated with entirely baseless or even degrading beliefs or practices. On the other hand, a man's whole experience may be permeated in reality by religion, although he disregards or rejects the forms of theological belief under which religion is usually represented.

We may first consider in detail the conception of truth. In the previous chapters the application to our experience of different modes of general interpretation has been discussed. What we call their truth lies in the degree of consistency with which they represent our experience, and we have seen that fundamental consistency becomes greater in biological than in mere physical interpretation, and greater in psychological than in biological interpretation. Individual psychological interpretation leaves us, however, with nothing which could be regarded as final truth, but only consistency within one personality among other personalities. Nevertheless an ideal of final truth is always before us, and the search for truth has a binding authority which all men acknowledge as a duty, however different in detail what is actually regarded as true may appear to different individuals.

The conception of truth, whether relative or ultimate, presupposes a world of one personality. For experience not regarded as unified in one personality there would be no meaning in truth as consistent in at least some degree with the whole of experience. Thus experience of truth as such is not only essentially personal, but presupposes a unified personal universe. We can argue, on the lines of certain of the Greek philosophers, that there can be no such thing as truth; but if this were so it would still be truth. Our regard for truth is in reality a part of ourselves, and we cannot escape from it any more than we can jump out of our own skins.

Truth must be consistent with our experience, and our experience, as we have seen, is in final analysis an experience of personality. But since we perceive other persons as well as ourselves, what can be regarded as true, even if it is only partial truth, must be true for them as well as ourselves, and must therefore be independent of mere individual personality. It is as individuals, however, that we experience the search after truth, and its authoritative character.

This implies, as already pointed out, that apparent individual personality is much more than mere individual personality, since the search for final truth is present in individual experience. The philosophical discussions in the previous chapters have shown that the universe of our experience is a universe of personality. There is no ultimate consistency, but only relative consistency, in any less comprehensive interpretation. The authority with which the search for final truth appeals is therefore a manifestation in us of personality embracing all individual personalities, and capable of rendering the partial interpretations of our experience fundamentally consistent with one another. This is what we refer to when we speak, in the language of religion, of divine truth, and use the word God to designate the all-embracing personality in whose existence ultimate reality exists.

For mere individual personality truth can have no real meaning; but in the trust in objective experience which is present to all, and which is the presupposition of all scientific investigation, God as all-embracing personality is revealed. In various forms of religious belief truth is represented as a revelation from without at some particular time or place, and not as something the nature of which is revealed in personal experience and which is constantly being revealed more adequately. This has brought these forms of religion into conflict with science and philosophy and placed them in what seems to me a position inconsistent with the personal revelation which is of the very essence of religion. Religion itself, and nothing less, leads science and philosophy to reject forms of belief which, in the guise of religion, are inconsistent with the rest of our experience. There is no inherent reason for conflict between science, philosophy, and religion, but conflict inevitably arises when either religion or science assumes an artificial and inadequate form. In this conflict it is in reality religion which is rejecting a foreign element within itself. In as far, however, as different forms of religion amount simply to a recognition of the all-embracing personality of God, they stand on firm ground which, as it seems to me, cannot be shaken.

Rudimentary religion has often taken on the form of polytheism, just as rudimentary psychology has divided up the unity of personality into various supposed separate faculties. In what may call itself atheistic religion the state, or ideal humanity, may be put in the place of God. Nevertheless true religion may exist under imperfect forms such as these, in so far as they supply sanctions for following after what is good in conduct, true, or beautiful. The reason why the monotheism represented in Jewish religion came to prevail is simply that it corresponds to both the unity and all-embracing character of the divine personality which reveals itself in our experience. In polytheism the unity is lacking, while in the other forms of religion just named the all-embracing character is absent.

Our ideal of what is true is not only a personal experience, but is independent of mere individual personality in any form. It depends neither on the personality of a mere individual nor on any form of group personality such as a state might represent. It sometimes happens that a state, or perhaps a religious organization, attempts to dictate to its members what shall be regarded as true. Such dictation may, perhaps, present certain temporary advantages of a practical character; but what is merely dictated in this manner has none of the binding authority which is the attribute of truth.

The difference between truth and what is regarded as mere individual interpretation appears everywhere in our ordinary experience. We cannot escape the conviction that the universe we experience is a real universe, although when we attempt to interpret it in terms merely of the conceptions of physical, biological, or psychological science it no longer appears as more than an imperfectly perceived or interpreted universe, not consistent, when so interpreted, with itself. It is only in so far as we can regard it also as a revelation in us, however imperfect, of God, that it assumes the character of self-consistent reality, so that the facts of our ordinary observation come to have the binding authority which all true science claims for them. However imperfect our interpretation of these facts may be, as already illustrated above, their authority as revealing reality remains, and the element of order which we find in them is from a truly religious standpoint divine. The observations on which the sciences are based embody what is sacred, and what, when fully interpreted, in relation to the rest of experience, appeals to all men.

It may appear as if we could attach no definite meaning to the conception of God as all-embracing Personality, and as if personality can only mean one personality among others. But on this point we can appeal to religious experience. For religion, and very definitely for Christian religion, God is present in the experiences of all men, and is the source of all higher aspirations. The idea of God as a being apart from other individual personalities is not, therefore, in accordance with religious experience. For religion God is actually present everywhere, was and will be at all times; and our universe is the progressive manifestation of God.

If we consider what the conception of even individual personality implies we find the same apparent difficulties as in the conception of all-embracing personality. A person is the expression of unity embracing what may be regarded as the separate personalities of innumerable cells or groups of cells present in the living body, but is no less real on this account. It is in our personal relations with other persons, with our search after truth, and with other forms of unity

which are independent of ourselves as mere individuals, that we become aware of the personality of
God.

But even if we admit all this we may ask in what
sense God could have existed at a time before not
only human beings, but any definitely recognized
forms of life, existed. For the Kantian philosophy
this question concerned a phenomenal universe, in
which time and space were only forms of perception,
and therefore within the universe of perception, so
that a gross *petitio principii* was made in imagining a
physical universe independent of perception of it.
For the post-Kantian philosophy represented in this
book Kant's phenomenal universe is no mere phenomenal universe of physical science, but a real universe, the manifestation of God's personality, and
independent of all mere individual personality. From
this standpoint a physical universe apart from God's
personality in it is an impossible assumption, just as an
unperceived physical universe would be from Kant's
standpoint. The fact that 'common sense' is ready to
make such an assumption is only an instance of the
various inconsistencies into which the common-
sense conception of a self-existent physical universe
leads us.

Although it is true that our trust in experience is a
revelation of the presence in us of God, it is quite
clearly true equally that this revelation is only partial.
In the detailed interpretation of our experience we are
liable to every sort of error or inconsistency, and it is

only when we consider the nature as a whole of the search for truth that this search appears as the revelation in us of God. Though in the search after truth the presence of God in man is revealed, yet man is much less than God, and man's perceptions must be regarded as falling indefinitely far short of those of God.

For man's perceptions, to take an instance, it might seem that before men or similar conscious beings were evolved, the spiritual existence represented in truth, beauty, and right could not exist, since they are meaningless apart from perception of them. But philosophy shows us that, however imperfectly we may realize it, they must exist in the perceptions and will of God, and that, apart from this, existence of any sort would be meaningless. It is only for the inconsistent mixture of opinions which we call common sense that existence independent of spiritual existence seems possible; and on this point philosophy and religion seem to me to be in agreement.

If we assume that existence apart from spiritual existence is real existence, and that what existed before man was evolved was no more than what physical and particularly astronomical investigation reveals, we cannot avoid the conclusions of materialism. But we have seen in the previous chapters that our experience of life and personality is not consistent with materialistic interpretation. It is in connexion with our own world, minute though it appears for astronomy, that our fundamental knowledge has been gained; and that knowledge includes, however imperfectly, the knowledge of God. It also shows us that the physical interpretation of our experience is only abstract interpretation which takes no account of the most important elements in it.

Thus we can admit to the fullest extent that what exists now is the outcome of the past, but we must reject the assumption that mere physical interpretation tells us anything more about the past than it does about the present. It tells us nothing essential about life or individual personality, or God as personality. For physical science these appear unintelligible or miraculous; and, as we have seen, the reason for this is that the working hypotheses of physical science are, from their nature, incapable of expressing our experience of life, personality, and God as personality.

Our own experience of life and individual personality seems to limit our experience to what is more or less immediately around us in space and time. But in our experience of goodness, truth, and beauty we escape from this limitation and attain to at least a glimpse of reality as the manifestation of God.

We are accustomed at present not merely to the correct assumption that the world which we see and feel around us is a real world, but that its nature is adequately represented by the interpretations of physical science. This book will have been written in vain if it has not made clear that physical science deals with only partial or abstract aspects of the reality. It is not through the study of physical science, but through that of human experience on our own planet, and in our own times, that we reach an adequate conception; and this is completely inconsistent with the materialism which accepts the physical interpretation as more than a quite partial interpretation.

Let us now consider the implications of what is regarded as right or good conduct. Right conduct is essentially bound up with truth. We have already seen that for personality what is perceived cannot be separated from what is willed. What is perceived has a motive character or is motivated, and voluntary action divorced from perception is without meaning. Personality extends over both volition and perception, and the conception of what is right or good in volition corresponds to the conception of what is true in perception. This, with its many implications, was already realized by Socrates in his discussions of the relations between knowledge and virtue.

We can make an artificial separation between what is perceived and what is willed, and, as we have already seen, we make a similar artificial separation in physical interpretation between cause and effect, matter and energy, or wherever in our ordinary experience we make use of the conceptions of traditional physical science. But the artificial character of this separation has already been pointed out in the preceding chapters, and the fundamental fact that the whole of our experience is an experience of personality. Our experience of the authority of what appears right, like our experience of the authority of what appears true, does not, however, depend on mere individual personality, and must therefore be regarded as a revelation in individual personality of the all-embracing personality of God. What appears right or a matter of duty has thus sacred authority, like what appears true.

From the mere standpoint of physical science a living organism appears as an extremely complex piece of physical and chemical machinery, responding continuously to physical and chemical events in its environment. From the less inadequate standpoint of biology, the life of an organism is a unity which actively maintains itself in a manner characteristic for each organism, the apparently separable physical and chemical events in the body of the organism, and in its environment, displaying persistent co-ordination in which this unity shows itself. From the still less inadequate standpoint of psychology, what is interpreted in biology as mere life, maintaining itself blindly without regard to past or future events, becomes personality, a unity within which the world is a perceived and willed world of objects and events, which in their mutual relationships, both spatial and temporal, express the unity. They are thus 'perceived' as with a past and potential future inseparable from their present, and not merely in their blind immediate relations, as part of mere life. The actions of a person are correspondingly determined or guided in continuous organic relation with past, present, and future, and so that what we now call his interest or personality is maintained. In both perception and action a person learns from experience, and predicts further experience and plans actions accordingly. In the conception of right action or duty, however, we are not dealing with mere individual interest or personality, but with what includes other interests or personalities.

Right conduct may be defined as conduct which is consistent with the legitimate interests of other persons and of societies of persons. Kant defined it as conduct capable of embodiment in law universal: but owing to the manner in which he had separated off the 'phenomenal' world of perception from what 'practical reason' deals with, he was unable to give this definition capacity for concrete application. For him duty appeared as something austerely and incomprehensibly separated from the world of ordinary perception. It is to the ordinary perceived and willed world of personality that our ideal of rightness or goodness applies, and what is right, like what is true, has no meaning apart from personality. The world of our experience appears to us as full of every sort of defect and wrong, just as it is full of every sort of obscurity. Right, therefore, appears to us, like truth, as only an incompletely realized ideal. But this does not prevent us from experiencing the authority of what appears to us as right. An ideal of right is present to all men, with an authority which all men acknowledge. In acknowledging its presence and compelling power it is the presence of what can be nothing less than all-embracing personality that we acknowledge, and this, in the language of religion, is the presence of God.

For religion God is ever present and active, amid all the evident chaos, evil, and obscurity of our experience; and the conviction of this brings with it strength and inward peace.

What we call a sense of duty, or of what is right, implies a realization not merely of other interests than our individual interests, but that we are bound in our conduct to have regard to them and promote them in so far as possible without interfering with other obligations. In this realization, under whatever name we call it, we are experiencing what for religion is the presence in us of all-embracing personality or God. We may not interpret it in this religious sense, but it seems impossible to interpret it rationally otherwise, and when it is interpreted definitely in a religious sense it becomes much clearer and more binding. It is therefore under the heading of religion that the subject of ethics is referred to in this book.

The realization of duty or responsibility is present in all our conscious behaviour, whether as voluntary actions or perceptions, so that they are controlled by it: it belongs to our inmost being and is not something imposed from without. As already pointed out, personality is free in as far as it is an effective expression of its own perceptions and motives, and in realizing and acting on duty an additional element of freedom is added, since it is we ourselves who recognize what is right. But the recognition of it is not recognition of mere individual personality, but of the presence within us of all-embracing personality or

God. This is what is implied in realizing the existence of duty, and doing it to the best of our very imperfect knowledge. The freedom we experience is divine freedom, and no contradiction exists between it and our own freedom. In this way we can reconcile, if we wish, the theological doctrine of divine determination with that of personal freedom.

There is no part of conscious behaviour to which responsibility does not attach. Man is not a playground for blind instincts and impulses which are inconsistent with his freedom and might thus be set up as an excuse for wrongdoing. It is also man himself who judges his own conduct, and awards punishment in the form of remorse, or reward in the form of inward peace.

From a biological standpoint man is the seat of innumerable blindly acting instincts, associated with equally blindly acting physiological activities, and showing no more than the co-ordination inherent in mere life. It is, however, the grossest mistake to accept as sufficient either this biological interpretation or an interpretation based only on the conception of individual personality. What for biological interpretation are no more than blind instincts are seen, from the ethical standpoint, to enter into what is sacred.

From no more than a biological standpoint the conduct implied in search for truth or regard for the interests of others represents only a functioning of the central nervous system and its associated organs. We can say the same of the love between man and woman or parent and child. But biological interpretation is totally insufficient to express the facts in any of these cases. They embody what is sacred, or if they do not do so they are a degradation. The application to them of a mere biological interpretation is not only incorrect, but in itself degrading; and this degrading influence is evident enough in psychological ideas which are common at the present time.

The conception of right or good conduct covers not merely our relations to other individuals as such, but also our relations to societies of individuals, and the relations of these societies to one another. As a mere society of individual persons, a state or other society has only the same significance as an individual person, but goodness or virtue covers not merely the relations of individuals to one another as individuals, but also their relations to societies or states, and the mutual relations of states.

The realization, for instance, that it is a duty to be a good and loyal citizen is the foundation of the ties of country, so that they enter into religion, in so far as the affairs of the country are conducted in accordance with what appears right towards its own citizens and other countries. But so far as this does not appear to be the case the duty of loyalty is overridden. The conception of right takes precedence of patriotism, just as the conception of truth takes precedence of loyalty to some overt form of religion or science. It is to God that allegiance is ultimately due, and neither a state nor church nor anything else can take the place of God. Except in so far as a state or church is an association of good individuals it has no real authority or stability. The state in the mere form of a 'leviathan' compelling its members is essentially unstable and more or less impotent.

A state may also be regarded as no more than an economic organization for promotion of the individual interests of its members. This conception fails, however, to express the fact that a state is founded, not on individual self-interest, but on mutual duties which are sacred.

We rely at every turn on honesty, charity, and sense of duty in others. Apart from the existence of these characters civilization of all kinds would disappear, and states would be utterly unstable in spite of the most elaborate systems of state laws.

A stable state is based on the freedom of its members, and this means, not absence of obligation on their part, but freedom to do what appears to them as right, and to co-operate with others in maintaining it. It also means tolerance and charity towards those who see differently what seems to them right; and the justification for this tolerance is the faith that God is present in all strivings after truth and right. For the same reason the state has a sacred duty to all its members who are striving to do the duties, however humble, which come to them.

The attempt is sometimes made to base the conception of right on either individual self-interest or the interest of a group personality, such as a state.

It is maintained that it is to the advantage of an individual or state to act according to a certain recognized code of conduct, and that the advantage thus arising to an individual or state is the basis of morality, or else that in a future world it will be an advantage. Such a conception does not, however, correspond with our experience of moral obligation. What we regard as right is something apart from mere individual interest, whether in the present or an assumed future world, and apart also from the interest of a state as a mere form of group personality.

Moral obligation has also been based on the pursuit of individual pleasure. To act rightly is certainly a pleasure or satisfaction. But pleasure itself is only self-realization, and if we take pleasure in caring for the interests of others the fact that it is a pleasure to do so is only another way of stating the fact that we do so voluntarily, and thus explains nothing.

We must now discuss what is implied in our recognition of beauty. In what is beautiful we recognize what authoritatively appeals, or is capable of appealing, to all men, quite apart from their mere individual interests, and as a value which it is a duty to maintain and further. There are endless varieties of beauty, and it is evident that the perception of them depends upon individual capacity.

A first question with regard to beauty might be whether it has any objective existence, or is merely something subjective. But we have already seen, in connexion with perception generally, that the separation of subjective and objective is impossible. In the perception of it our universe is also made, as Kant pointed out with regard to the perceived physical universe. In the perception of it beauty is certainly also made; but this character is common to the whole of our world of experience. That world is a personal or concrete spiritual world, and its spiritual character is specially evident in the existence of what is beautiful. Hence the beauty which we perceive is no less real than what we are accustomed to interpret physically.

But since beauty, like goodness and truth, has the character of appealing to all men, independently of their individual interests or personalities, we must regard the perception of it, just as in the cases of goodness and truth, as a manifestation in us of all-embracing personality, so that it represents divine perception, and exists, like truth, whether or not it is perceived by mere individual persons. In our perceptions of beauty, and particularly perhaps of beauty in Nature, we are participating directly in divine perception, however imperfectly.

Beauty is thus no mere subjective illusion, but, fleeting as its forms are, something intensely real, though we only see it imperfectly, and it is often only revealed to us at all by poets, artists, musical composers, and writers who have seen aspects of it and been able to represent them to us. We are living in an epoch in which spiritual reality of every kind is clouded over by our materialism, so that we scarcely know what to make of beauty, however much we may feel it. But we can look forward to a time when the clouds of materialism will have passed away, though that time can hardly come until philosophy itself comes into its own.

It is evident that in the perception of beauty what we perceive embodies inherently co-ordinated unity, the details existing, in both space-relations and time-relations, as expressions of the whole, while the unity exists only as expressing the existence of the details. But this inherently co-ordinated unity can exist only in perception which extends over time-relations as well as space-relations, as, for instance, in the beauty of a living organism, a poem, a piece of music, or a picture, where the beauty appears as we take in the details one by one.

What we see as beautiful seems at first sight to be altogether different from what we see as right or true; but, as it appears to the writer, right conduct, truth, and beauty are only different aspects of what is fundamentally the same. Right conduct embodies co-ordinated unity which can be, and often is, called beautiful. It also embodies truth, as standing for a true perception of the relations between different individuals. Similarly truth, as being essentially motivated, involves not only a true realization of co-ordinated relations, but also practical use of the knowledge of them. In a similar way beauty involves both truth or right perception and the co-ordinated unity which we find also in right conduct.

It is clear, however, that what appears beautiful need not also represent what appears either as good or as true in the sense of representing reality. It only represents co-ordinated wholeness which is independent of individual self-interest, though it must represent this wholeness truly or effectively. But what we call truth, goodness, and beauty are in themselves only partial realizations of the search after truth, goodness, and beauty. Truth, for instance, in the sense of physical or biological science, is only partial truth, as we have seen. Beauty and goodness are similarly only partial. The partial realizations need not, and do not, agree. Where the agreement lies is in the realization, however partial, of co-ordinated wholeness, and this we can recognize as the common divine element in the seeking after truth, goodness, and beauty.

Nevertheless, it seems to me that the highest forms of beauty embody both truth and goodness, though these forms of beauty are the most difficult to discover or represent, and are often marred by insufficient regard for truth.

From a physical standpoint a picture is nothing but a collection of daubs of paint possessing different physical and chemical characters, and so arranged that when illuminated it presents a similar optical appearance to some physical object or collection of objects. But if it is also beautiful its beauty has from this standpoint no meaning, since its parts and what they represent are regarded as essentially independent of one another. When the picture is beautiful, both its artistic details and what they represent embody inherent co-ordinated unity which exists, or may exist, for all men, whatever their merely individual interests may be.

In beauty we recognize something which is distinguishable from goodness of conduct in that, except in the duty of preserving and furthering it, it need not refer to conduct. We find beauty in a flower, a landscape, a sunset, or the stars, just as we may find it in an individual person or any of his handiwork. Nevertheless beauty as co-ordinated unity embracing both space-relations and time-relations can have no meaning except in personality; and as beauty appeals to all persons, it is nothing less than a manifestation of all-embracing personality—a witness to the existence of God. Its recognition in both perception and conscious behaviour is thus part of religion, and it is so treated in this book.

We can see readily how portraiture in painting and sculpture, or how poetical or dramatic or architectural art express personality. Music also, must, I think, be regarded as fundamentally an expression of the personal emotion which is just as real as the otherwise perceived events which express personality. The expression is, or may be, in unarticulated form, and only in simultaneous and successive notes of sound. When, however, we consider the beauty in surrounding Nature, it might seem, at first sight, as if this beauty were something apart from personality.

The beauty of a landscape, or of a flower, seems like something independent of personality. But for our awareness of divine personality we should have to consider it so, and it would appear as a standing contradiction that beauty, to which no meaning can be attached apart from personality, should nevertheless exist in an impersonal form. When, however, we realize the existence of divine personality, and the revelation of it, however imperfectly, in ourselves, the apparent contradiction disappears, and we can still regard the beauty in Nature as a manifestation of personality. It is, indeed, when we perceive it, a direct revelation in us of divine personality.

The surrounding world of Nature is no mere physico-chemical or biological world, but a world in which personality is just as much embodied as in our own bodies. For certain practical purposes we can regard it as a mere physico-chemical or biological world, but as the world of our experience it is not only a world of personality but also of divine personality. The beauty which we see in it is an expression of the unity of personality, apart from which we can attach no meaning to beauty. But when we see this beauty it is not as an expression of mere individual personality—as what is useful or pleasing to me—but as revealing, perhaps as only a glimpse, all-embracing personality, just as it is revealed in a good action or a demonstration of fuller truth.

In beauty, therefore, whether in art or in Nature, there is a divine element, so that the perception of beauty enters into religion, and aesthetics cannot be discussed fundamentally apart from religion. Art in various forms, such as music, architecture, and painting, has always been associated as a matter of fact with the ordinary recognition of religion. It is just as natural that all forms of science, or the pursuit of truth, should be associated with, or form part of, religion. But the clash which arose in Renaissance times between religious beliefs and science led to a separation between science and religion; and except in missionary enterprises this separation, which is a direct outcome of inadequate or antiquated religious and scientific creeds, remains. The separation of educational or scientific from religious activities seems altogether artificial, but for the present cannot be avoided in name, though it scarcely exists in reality.

Regard for beauty shows itself not merely in various forms of art, but in many homely virtues such as cleanliness, tidiness, good dressing and furnishing, or cultivation of flowers. Though we do not usually think of these virtues as connected with religion, yet the connexion is a very real one. Religion is sometimes expressed in them more clearly than in other ways.

To pass to another aspect of religion, the special feature of Christianity has been, as it seems to me, its teaching that God is no mere perfect self-existent being, but present in and not separated from the evil of our world. The actual world is anything but perfect, and for a theology which assumes both perfection and omnipotence in God, the existence of imperfection, suffering, and sin would seem to present an insoluble problem.

This raises the question of what we can mean by either perfection or corresponding omnipotence in the conception of God. We can imagine a machine which is perfect or almost perfect as regards the manner in which it fulfils its design. But the same conception cannot be applied to living personality, because the very idea of personality involves, as already pointed out, a continuous struggle with imperfection. Divine perfection does not consist in such perfection as we may find in the working of a machine, but in the fact that the manifestations of God consist in the active realizations of goodness, truth, and beauty. Divine omnipotence, similarly, does not consist in the perfect control of a machine, but in the ultimate power of goodness, truth, and beauty, which embody the love of God.

When we look back on the argument running through the previous chapters we can see that the guiding conceptions discussed in each chapter would have no meaning except in relation to what in other respects remains unintelligible or chaotic. The conceptions of matter and energy, for instance, depend on what is found to remain constant in presence of what are and remain otherwise fleeting appearances. The conception of life depends, in its application, on the co-ordination which is found to persist amidst what are otherwise unco-ordinated physical and chemical phenomena, so that physical interpretation is presupposed in biological interpretation. Similarly, biological and therefore also physical interpretation must be present in psychological interpretation. In all these cases, therefore, the interpretation includes a negative element. Coming now to religious interpretation, we can see that the conception of God would have no meaning apart from what appears as a world of mere individual personality, or of physical or biological existence. It is in the continuous superseding of what is imperfect, obscure, or evil that the reality and love of God appear in the manifestations of goodness, beauty, and truth. Thus in apparent individual personality, with all its defects and limitations, we find the manifestation of God as all-embracing Personality. The kingdom of God is within us, so that all our experience is transformed, and it no longer appears as that of a universe of mere individual personality, or a corresponding economic world, and much less as a mere biological or physical universe, but as a universe to which the active manifestation of divine personality gives its reality and meaning.

Kant's conception of a phenomenal physical universe embodied also the conception of an unknown and unknowable noumenal universe. This was necessary in order to explain the insufficiency of physical conceptions to account for what remained unintelligible in the physical universe. Later German philosophy abolished the noumenal world as such, but failed in resolving the actual universe into nothing more than an ideal universe. For Christian and other theologies the existence of a devil or other malignant power, or simply 'the flesh', may be said to occupy the place of Kant's noumenal world. The actual universe is not represented as ideally perfect or intelligible, and is clearly not ideally perfect or intelligible. The conception of a completely intelligible or perfect universe or God turns out to be meaningless, since it is only in presence of what remains imperfect or unintelligible that the attributes of God as personal and active manifest themselves. The imperfection remains, and will always remain, since it belongs to the nature of spiritual reality. The evil in our universe may seem to be diminishing in the course of evolution, but it is always also becoming more evident to us, and we must look backwards in history as well as forwards if we wish to avoid distorted views.

It is not in progress towards a utopian future, but in the world as it actually exists that we find the manifestation of God. In facing its evils courageously and doing all we can to overcome them as they appear to us, God is present in us.

We can thus see that truth, goodness, and beauty exist only in relation to what is not, or is not yet, true, good, and beautiful. Science is a continuous struggle against ignorance, goodness is a continuous struggle against what is not good, and beauty is a realization of itself in what is not otherwise beautiful, such as paint or stone or sounds, or the material aspects of Nature. Truth, goodness, and beauty do not, as Plato thought, or as in reality Hegel thought, exist as impersonal ideas, but as the concrete manifestations of active divine personality.

Were it the case that regard for truth compelled us to conceive our universe of experience as simply a physically interpreted universe arranged spatially and temporally in the manner which physical science postulates, religion as the embodiment of truth would lead us to accept this interpretation, though it would represent an utterly truncated form of religion, and at the same time an utterly truncated interpretation of experience. This would still be so if regard for truth compelled us to accept as ultimately true an interpretation in terms of biology or of individual psychology. But we have seen that none of these interpretations can be accepted as ultimately consistent, though they are all stepping-stones in the direction of truth. The existence of our own regard for truth, goodness, and beauty reveals to us the real nature and all-embracing personality of God.

The outcome of the foregoing discussion is that we find in our experience a manifestation of the personality of God. Religion is the recognition of this fact, in both what we perceive and what we do. In reality the recognition enters into the whole of our experience, quite apart from overt recognition as religion. Overt recognition, however, gives us strength and courage in following after what is right, true, and beautiful; and the influence of existing religious organizations, in spite of inadequate creeds, is due to this fact. Overt recognition, in so far as it stands for real religion, is a factor which gives stability to a nation in which it exists, since it strengthens all that makes for loyal citizenship and friendly relations with other nations. Should war nevertheless come in what appears as a good cause, overt religion gives a nation greatly increased courage and strength, though the whole influence of true religion is in a direction which makes for peace and friendship between nations.

Let us now examine more fully the sources of weakness, which are very evident, in overt religion as it at present exists in European civilization. We can, I think, trace this weakness in the main to the confused philosophical ideas which came into prominence with the development of physical science in Renaissance times, though these confused ideas were inherent in previous philosophy or theology, including Greek philosophy.

If our visible and tangible universe is nothing but the universe as represented by traditional physical science, religion seems meaningless in our interpretation of its behaviour. We may regard it as originally created by God, but this makes no practical present difference. Moreover, we are left with no convincing grounds for assuming God's existence in any sense which corresponds to that of religion. Even if we regard ourselves as autonomous or free, we appear to be surrounded by a brute and senseless universe of matter and void, and the idea of our freedom is hard to defend. Experiment is commonly taken to confirm the physical conception, which has thus come to appear as a matter of common sense, accepted by religious and irreligious alike.

Religion has nevertheless survived in so far as it is concerned with human behaviour, but in an attenuated form reflecting the materialism of the physical interpretation. The old conception, according to which in all, or at any rate much, of what is visible and tangible the direct manifestation of God is present, has given place to that of an invisible and intangible spiritual world; but the more the apparent reality of the material world is realized, the more difficult does it become to believe in the reality of the spiritual world. We seem to be surrounded and shut in by a physical universe in both space and time. The occurrence in the past of miraculous events and revelations is still taught as an integral part of religion, but the fact that it is so taught is more and more a source of weakness in proportion as the improbability of such events, and the lack of valid evidence of their having occurred, become more and more apparent.

The discussions in the previous and present chapters have shown that the visible and tangible universe is much more than what can be interpreted in terms of traditional physical science, however useful in many respects such partial interpretation is. The ultimate interpretation is the spiritual interpretation for which all that is clearly definable in the visible and tangible world is the manifestation of God. The materialistic interpretation is not a possible one, nor is it compatible with religion.

In so far, therefore, as overt religion has accepted the materialistic interpretation, it has accepted what is inconsistent with religion, the result being what has already been referred to. But this is no longer the case when we only accept the results of physical science as a partial interpretation. Not only is religion then compatible with the legitimate conclusions of natural science, but the faithful and fearless prosecution of natural science as a contribution to relative truth is a part of religion itself. Faithfulness to observation has all the sacred characters of religion, whether or not it is called by the name of religion.

As it appears to me, it is the materialism which has penetrated religion that has led to the survival in theology of a belief in miraculous events, in spite of the development of historical criticism and scientific knowledge. Religion has no need of miracles. As soon as we realize that our ordinary visible and tangible world is not the world of materialism but a spiritual universe in which God is everywhere revealed, the need for miraculous events disappears. But until a belief in them ceases to be regarded as a part of religion this belief will, to an increasing extent, hinder the acceptance of Christianity. On those who still insist on the miraculous element in religion a very heavy responsibility lies.

For my own part I look forward to a time when the occurrence of miraculous events will have ceased to form a part of Christian theology; but until this is brought about, anything which could be called orthodox Christianity will be impossible to a large and constantly increasing number of educated persons.

Let us consider what is meant by a miraculous event. We cannot, in the first place, regard it as an event which is incapable of being interpreted in terms of physical or chemical theory. If so, such events as the development of a plant from its seed would be miraculous. Nor can we regard it as an event which cannot be interpreted in terms of biology or individual psychology, since our experience of truth, goodness, and beauty cannot be so interpreted. The real meaning of a miraculous event is an event which cannot be repeated so that the possibility of its occurrence can be verified. When we cannot repeat and so verify the possibility of an event, it becomes too improbable to be credible, and particularly so if such historical evidence as exists of its occurrence is, like the Christian traditions of miraculous events, extremely weak. It is religion in the form of a seeking after the consistency which constitutes truth that leads us to disbelieve the existence of miraculous events. In any case religion and our belief in God is in no way dependent on belief in miraculous events, and it is in our ordinary experience that God is revealed to us.

Associated with religion we usually find belief in an individual future existence. If we accept the common assumption that the visible and tangible world is nothing but a physical world, while apart from it, though somehow interacting with it, is a spiritual world, it would seem that if we admitted that the spirit perishes with the body we have at the same time abandoned belief in the spiritual world. The present epoch of European civilization is specially characterized by the common-sense belief that, whatever is true of a spiritual universe, the universe as interpreted physically is at any rate real. With this belief widespread, but accompanied by belief in spiritual reality, it is inevitable that common sense should postulate, as for instance Descartes did, an individual soul existing independently of a material body, however difficult this assumption may prove to be. It is equally inevitable that the physical universe should not be regarded as embodying spiritual reality, and that God should be regarded as existing apart from what is taken to be only physical reality.

Hence it comes that mere individual immortality seems a necessary postulate unless we give up belief in a spiritual universe; and for materialism immortality is of course meaningless. When, however, we realize that not only is the personality of God manifested in our whole universe, but that we ourselves, in so far as we strive after what is divine, are partakers, however imperfectly, in divine personality, and in this regard immortal, mere individual immortality ceases to have its former apparent significance.

As mere individuals we are changing, and thus transient, like all other partial manifestations of God under the forms of space and time. The vanished touch, and the voice that is silent, have gone for ever at death. But God, as the reality of the personality which they expressed, is still present, so that the real personality is unaffected by death. In virtue of the presence of God in us we, too, are immortal, and religious belief in immortality has thus its full justification. In the face of death we can rest in God.

It may be that, though we believe this, it will for the present seem a far-away intellectual belief, which does not take the place of the ordinary theological form of the belief in immortality. On the other hand, the latter belief, when we attempt to give it definite form, becomes entirely shadowy, and of this we are becoming more and more clearly aware with the advance of knowledge. That this belief is the counterpart of a materialistic interpretation of our perceived universe is evident, but it is not a belief which can be brought into relation with scientific knowledge of any kind. In its existing form we must, I think, regard it as a remnant of a partial materialism which once seemed consistent with the rest of our experience, but which does so no longer. It is hard to rid ourselves of the materialistic atmosphere which at present surrounds us.

Nevertheless the conception of personal immortality is an essential part of religion, following from the religious recognition of divine personality in human personality; and I have attempted in the foregoing discussion to show how this recognition is an essential element in our experience.

God's existence cannot be regarded as depending

in any way on man's existence, although it is in man's own existence that God's existence is revealed to man. We can imagine a time when no human beings or organisms of comparable development existed, or when beings of greatly superior development will exist, in whom God's existence will appear much more fully. But we know enough at present to be sure that in existence in any form God must be manifested as all-embracing personality, and that the course of evolution must represent a more and more detailed divine manifestation. Apart from God's existence as living and active, reality has no ultimate meaning. However far we may look backwards in time we cannot reach a time when the ordered beauty of the heavens—that beauty which seems overwhelming when we contemplate it—was not present. The existence of truth, order, and beauty are eternal, as God is eternal, though the particular form of order which we designate as right conduct was undeveloped, just as it is undeveloped in a human embryo or infant.

For Kant's philosophy the existence of mind was something essentially shadowy, as a general condition under the forms of which the phenomenal physical world assumes definiteness. To this extent his philosophy was idealistic, and the idealistic element in it was further developed by his successors in Germany, particularly Hegel. It is not, however, to idealism, but to what might be called spiritual realism, that the reasoning contained in this book has led. What is called realism has usually stood for the acceptance of the physical interpretation of experience as representing reality, but it is realism in a much deeper sense that I have tried to represent. We have been led to a conception which might be taken as embodying what was essentially true in Spinoza's philosophy, and equally in the philosophy of Berkeley.

In his two later books, the *Critique of Judgement* and the *Critique of Practical Reason*, Kant in reality broke down the chains of mechanical necessity which he had forged, as regards the perceived world, in his *Critique of Pure Reason*. In spite of his conclusions in the latter Critique, he based his final religious conclusions on our actual ethical experience.

Various systems of religious belief represent religion with varying degrees of indefiniteness or incompleteness, corresponding more or less to the stages of culture reached by different peoples. Among Western peoples Christianity displaced, but largely also absorbed, the existing forms of 'pagan' religion, though pre-Christian Jewish religion has survived in a very remarkable manner. Mohammedan religion also displaced and absorbed more primitive religious beliefs in parts of Europe and large parts of Asia and Africa.

There is no reason to suppose that Christianity will not continue to survive. It seems evident, however, that in order to survive and develop it must harmonize itself with the development of culture in other directions. That it is doing so is evident enough; but the main hindrance is, it appears to me, the materialism which prevails in the ordinary present-day interpretation of our universe, and which penetrates Christian theology. Christianity must rid itself of materialism and be ready to cope with materialism and any other forms of anti-religious ideas if it is to survive and at the same time retain or regain the adherence of a large part of the educated classes.

We can probably say the same of other great religious systems, and at the same time anticipate that they and Christianity will gradually come closer together. There are at present many signs of this.

If we accept as more than partial truth the scientific interpretation of our experience, religion becomes meaningless and inconsistent with the rest of experience. The reasoning which is summarized in this book shows, however, that scientific interpretation, whether mathematical, physical, biological, or psychological, is only partial, since it leaves out of account essential features in the experience which it describes. Unless it did so it would, however, not only be of no practical use, but would cease to reveal the partial truth which it does actually reveal. When we realize that scientific interpretation is only an abstract or partial form of interpretation we can see also that confusion must result from introducing religious considerations into its mere details.

There is partial truth in the view which presents not only human affairs, but also all life, as insignificant happenings in a physical universe of unknown vastness in space and time. From the standpoint of philosophy and religion this view leads to a wholesome correction of inadequate conceptions of personality and of God. There is also partial truth in the view which presents human behaviour as an expression of the play of blind animal instincts. This view, too, leads to a wholesome correction of narrow and inadequate conceptions of personality. Similarly there is partial truth in the view of death as an end of conscious existence. For religion, the fact, not only of death, but also of birth, is a constant reminder that personality is more than mere individual personality.

In the development of modern philosophy it has appeared as if philosophy were something apart from both science and religion, though sometimes, at least, mediating between them. The reasoning developed in the present chapter leads, however, to the conclusion that philosophy results in both science and religion being purified from the materialistic elements which intrude themselves into existing science and theology. Thus philosophy becomes a support to religion by clarifying it, but is certainly not a mere 'handmaid' to existing theological beliefs. Against the materialistic elements in these beliefs, philosophy presents just as firm a front as does science from another angle. It is only in so far as religion corresponds with what is most fundamental in experience that philosophical criticism becomes a support to it.

RETROSPECT

Lᴇᴛ us look back on, and endeavour to summarize, the train of reasoning which has run through the preceding chapters. The book began by pointing out the need for philosophy which arose in modern times, mainly from the apparent conflict between the conclusions of physical science and hitherto accepted theological and other conclusions as to spiritual existence. The attempts during the seventeenth and eighteenth centuries by Descartes and succeeding philosophical writers to reach consistent conclusions on these subjects were described generally in Chapter I. It was pointed out that these attempts focused themselves in the philosophical writings of Kant, who concluded that the visible and tangible universe is no less a construction of mind than a manifestation of external reality independent of perceiving mind. The perceived universe is thus only a 'phenomenal' universe, and it is only this 'phenomenal' universe that is represented in the universe of physical science. Beyond it there must be a 'noumenal' world of real existence, but which cannot be perceived.

Kant proceeded to analyse what he regarded as the contributions of mind to this phenomenal universe, and enumerated them as the general forms of perception, space and time, and various 'categories' such as the conceptions of quality, quantity, substance, and causality. But his assumption of a noumenal world, his separation of the forms and categories as independent of one another, and the adequacy of his enumeration of them, were criticized by his successors, and Hegel attempted to trace a logical development of the system of categories. The development of physical science itself in recent years, particularly in the hands of Einstein and Planck, has meanwhile tended to show more and more clearly that certain fundamental conceptions of physical science cannot be regarded as independent of one another. Thus we cannot regard space as independent of time or of motion of bodies. Nor, apparently, can we regard mass as independent of motion, since what we are led to regard as the most elementary units of mass must also be regarded as expressions of elementary co-ordinated motion. Fundamental physical science has thus ceased to be what not only Kant, but physicists in general, took it to be up to the close of the nineteenth century. It is no longer what can be described as mechanical science: and apart from other criticisms, Kant's reasoning, in so far as it assumed physical science to be essentially mechanical, falls to the ground. In other respects, however, Kant's general conclusions as to the impossibility of regarding the perceived world as independent of mind remain just as valid as ever they were. He showed finally, as it appears to me, that the conception of a visible and tangible universe independent of mind is without meaning, though as to the nature of mind, except as a unifying principle which cannot be identified with mere individual mind, this reasoning tells us nothing.

In Chapter II another aspect was discussed of the influence of natural science on modern thought. Kant's general conclusions as to the phenomenal perceived world left no place for biological science in this world except as a branch of ordinary physical science, and using the corresponding mechanical interpretations. In this respect he was in agreement with Descartes, who, in natural science, has come to be regarded as the founder of the mechanistic biology which became so prevalent in the latter part of the nineteenth century, and is still quite commonly regarded as scientifically orthodox.

Only a certain proportion of those who have specially studied living organisms have ever accepted the conception that the visible and tangible phenomena of life can be regarded as the expression of physical and chemical processes. From the time of Descartes onwards to the middle of last century the conception usually adopted by biologists and representatives of physical science was that though outside the bodies of living organisms the interpretations of the physical sciences hold good, the characteristic phenomena inside living parts are a manifestation of what was variously described as a soul acting unconsciously, a 'vital principle', or 'vital force'. The reasons for this conclusion, known as 'vitalism', were evident. A living organism preserves and reproduces its characteristic form and activities in a manner which is not recognizable outside living organisms, and cannot be interpreted in accordance with the conceptions of physical science.

Vitalism, however, was not a coherent conception. In one case after another phenomena which had been attributed to the vital principle were shown to be dependent on the influence of environmental conditions. This led to the general abandonment of vitalism in the latter half of last century, but left the characteristic features of life entirely obscure. The origin and maintenance of life would be a mystery, becoming constantly deeper the more we investigate it, if we accepted as more than provisional the ordinary physical interpretation of the perceived world, or Kant's account of it. There is no need, however, for this acceptance, and, as shown fully in Chapter II, the life of an organism must be regarded as an objective active unity which embraces its environment, and manifests itself not merely in the mutual relations between the parts of the organism itself, but also between the organism and its environment. The use of this conception in biology separates it from the physical sciences, and just as we seem to perceive a physical world in the light of physical conceptions, so do we seem to perceive the same world as a world of lives in terms of biological conceptions.

We are accustomed to assume that it is a physical world that our senses reveal to us. But when we examine more closely we find, as pointed out in Chapter II, that the details of what is thus revealed are determined by their relations to the rest of what is similarly revealed and to what else is happening in connexion with our bodies, and that our sense of the reality of what we perceive depends on the persistency of these relations in what we call a normal manner. In every respect in which an organism is related to its environment we find similarly that the details of the relationship depend on the normal maintenance of the organism's life.

The apparent physical world thus appears as a biological world of lives. The vitalists made the fatal mistake of accepting physical interpretation as a final interpretation of an organism's environment. In reality biological interpretation extends over the environment, and what had appeared as physical reality appears for biology as biological reality.

Biological interpretation corresponds more fundamentally to experience than physical interpretation, but takes no account of certain essential features in experience. We cannot interpret our own experience as that of mere living organisms responding blindly in the maintenance of life. The fact that our experience is conscious and voluntary implies much more than the fact that we are living organisms. In conscious experience it is not a mere immediate present that we perceive, but a world of objects embodying relationships to one another and to ourselves both spatially and temporally. What we perceive is also an expression, not merely of our life, but of the wider unity extending over time, which we call our interest or personality. Each distinguishable element in what we perceive is related to the other elements as embodying our interest, and has a corresponding motive relation to them, which expresses itself in voluntary activity. To act from a motive is thus to act as an expression of personality. The idea that in acting from a motive we are determined by something outside ourselves is thus wholly mistaken, and arises through the application to psychological phenomena of physical conceptions which are quite incapable of being so applied.

The world of our experience becomes now a psychological or concrete spiritual world of personalities. Personality extends over the whole of experience. It extends both outward and inward in space relations, and both backward and forward in time relations. It is thus in its own universe that personality is present, and not in a foreign physical universe. The world of personality is no mere attenuated soul apart from body and environment, but a concrete world which is both perceived and willed—the world of persons and their interests. The conception of it as a physical world is an abstraction of great practical use for certain limited practical purposes, but not more than a very partial representation of experience.

This brings us to the subject of religion. Personality may be regarded as the mere individual personality of one person or group of persons among others, and as that of a person who is born and dies. But consideration of our experience shows that personality implies much more. Our interest extends into the interests of other personalities, and over a past and future beyond the apparent time limits of individual personality. It includes the striving after right or good conduct, which is far more than an expression of mere individual interest. It also includes the search after truth, which, even though the truth is only partial, has binding authority for all personalities : also the perception and furtherance of beauty, which appeals to all, regardless of their individual interests. We find also that right, truth, and beauty are essentially one. We cannot interpret these features in any other way than that all-embracing personality manifests itself in individual personality, and that in this all-embracing personality is summed up the reality of our experience. The personality of God is indispensable in the final interpretation of our experience as revealing reality.

Religion is the recognition of all-embracing personality as God. The recognition of God in religion is no mere theoretical recognition, but includes the practical recognition of the search after right, truth, and beauty as of binding authority which is everywhere supreme, and overrides all mere individual interest or group interest. We cannot separate religion from this practical recognition; and the lives of good men, whether their goodness has shown itself mainly in faithfulness to the helping of others, or to the furthering of truth, or of beauty, are a standing witness to the existence of God.

If religion were taken to imply that God not only exists, but is also omnipotent and perfect, this conception would be contradicted at once by all the imperfection, sorrow, and sin which we see around us. But in actual religion, as distinguished from theological systems, we do not find this conception. It is in an otherwise chaotic world that God is revealed, just as it is in an otherwise chaotic world that the relative truths of science are revealed. The manifestation of divine will in the universe would have no meaning as living and active except in so far as the universe is at the same time chaotic or undefined. Religion does not explain away the chaos, which is a background apart from which God could not be conceived as living, loving, and active. For Christianity in particular, it is in the world of sorrow and sin that God is present, and to this conception, which has a universal appeal, the special strength of Christian theology is due. But the background of ignorance, ugliness, sorrow, and sin remains, and seems to become even more evident with the growing manifestation in it of God.

It will now be evident enough that instead of beginning the discussion of philosophy with physical science we might equally well have begun with some other branch of science, or, as Socrates in effect did in his discussion of 'virtue' and knowledge, with religion, by describing the fundamental experience which religion embodies. We could then, as Socrates did not himself do, have passed in succession to psychology, biology, physical science, and mathematics. These sciences would then represent successive stages in which our experience is stripped more and more of its actual content by a process of artificial abstraction.

The question would then remain as to why we apply this process of abstraction, and the answer given was that in matters of detail our perceptions are so imperfect that we are unable to reach more than abstract or imperfect conceptions. Yet these abstract conceptions are of the utmost service, so that we cannot dispense with them. They are nevertheless only our own devices, and if, as Descartes and many others have done, we regard them as complete representations of experience, confusion necessarily results, as shown in detail in the preceding chapters.

All of these sciences neglect elements in our experience, mathematical interpretation neglecting most, and psychological interpretation least. On the other hand mathematical or physical interpretations are far more frequently applicable in matters of detail than psychological interpretation, and in this respect are of very great importance. We can count and measure all sorts of aspects of our experience, but even when we can add a physical interpretation this by itself tells us nothing about biological significance or about values, though it may nevertheless be sufficient for many practical purposes where we do not require to see more deeply. From the standpoint of philosophy, however, the important matter is to realize that in whatever way we may approach philosophy the sciences represent reality only partially, so that their results must not be taken for more than this partial representation.

We have now reached the end of this outline of present-day philosophy as it appears to the writer. The general conclusions reached may be summed up in the statement that the real universe is a universe of personality and the progressive manifestation of God, its scientific aspects being only partial interpretations of it, the imperfect nature of which is revealed by philosophical criticism.

The book represents, as shortly as seemed possible, the reasoning which has guided me in the course of a struggle, begun in early manhood, and continued throughout an active scientific life, with the apparent contradictions which we find in our experience when we compare different aspects of it. In my own special subject, that of physiology, these apparent contradictions leap to the surface, as shown in Chapter II. We can live at peace with ourselves, without philosophy, if we are dealing with only one aspect of our experience, such as that of mathematics, physics, or chemistry. But it is otherwise when we try to reconcile different aspects. We require philosophy, and this differs entirely from the common plan of ignoring the existence of any aspect which we do not see how to reconcile with our own special aspect. Philosophy is assuredly not something which can be neglected.

PRINTED IN
GREAT BRITAIN
AT THE
UNIVERSITY PRESS
OXFORD
BY
JOHN JOHNSON
PRINTER
TO THE
UNIVERSITY